HOW TO SURVIVE

The Male~Menopause

Geoffrey Aquilina Ross is a freelance author and journalist who worked as a feature writer on male fashion and grooming for the *Evening Standard* for many years. He is a regular contributor to leading magazines and is London editor of the international magazine *L'Uomo Vogue* (Italy). He lives in London and Malta.

'A serious book, worth reading by all but the 20% who grow old without ever falling victims to M-M.' – *British Medical Journal*

HOW TO SURVIVE
The Male~

Menopause

by Geoffrey Aquilina Ross

ELM TREE BOOKS · LONDON

By the same author

Travel: *Malta, Gozo and Comino – all you need to know*

First published in Great Britain 1984
by Elm Tree Books/Hamish Hamilton Ltd
Garden House 57-59 Long Acre London WC2E 9JZ
First published in this edition 1985

Book design by Norman Reynolds
Drawings by Beryl Sanders

British Library Cataloguing in Publication Data

Aquilina Ross, Geoffrey
How to survive the male menopause.
1. Climacteric
I. Title
612′.665 RC884

ISBN 0-241-11168-4
ISBN 0-241-11442-X Pbk

Filmset by Pioneer
Printed in Great Britain by
St Edmundsbury Press, Bury St Edmunds, Suffolk

Contents

Acknowledgements
To all the doctors, analysts and therapists in London and New York who in the preparation of this book so freely gave their help, recommendations and facts based on innumerable case histories, and, to the many men (and sometimes their wives) who, having passed through the stages of the male-menopause, were able to confirm the facts by their own experience, my grateful thanks and lasting appreciation. Without their invaluable interest, friendship, concern and assistance many of us would be a lot less wise.

PART I

On what it is and what it is not

Introduction

For the vast majority of men in the Western world the male-menopause is no joke. They may not know they have it or have had it or, indeed, that it exists, but for a lengthy period of their forties the male-menopause is responsible for injecting a considerable amount of havoc and unrest into their lives. Married, single, divorced, heterosexual or gay, it affects all men alike. For some it strikes about the thirty-ninth birthday, for others any time into their late forties. It lasts about four years. Therapists today estimate that only twenty per cent of the Western male population avoid its disturbing effects.

But whereas the female menopause is physical and strikes women between the ages of forty-five and fifty-five as their menstrual cycle ceases, the male-menopause (the M-M) is a specifically emotional condition with a few physical side effects caused by reaction to the symptoms and the natural signs of physical deterioration due to aging as additional depressing factors.

Men do not have a menstrual cycle nor (whatever old wives tales may say) do they lose their sexual and reproductive powers through hormone change the way women do, so the words *male-menopause* may be considered something of a misnomer. The terms *mid-life anxiety* and *mid-life transition* both give a fair idea of what the problem is but neither one seems to have a sufficiently evocative ring. *Male-menopause* nicely sums up the problems of a seemingly inevitable and irrational mid-life crisis that can suddenly descend on a man as he stands on the threshold of middle age.

Spotting the problems brought on by M-M and identifying the cause can be difficult. A man's reaction to the symptoms can be mild, shakingly disruptive or, for many, severe. Which he gets is a matter of luck but invariably M-M begins with an illogical but consuming urge for change linked to an irrational but constant sense of frustration and depression. It might be a change of work or career that is needed, or, in a marriage or stable relationship, this urge for change may be a wild and desperate need to swap partners and seek out rejuvenating sexual encounters with younger friends. It is at this point many in the United States consider that marriages head irrevocably for the rocks.

The fact is that unless they recognize and admit to the symptoms most men usually feel isolated and little realize their contemporaries are being afflicted by similar, almost irrational, anxieties and problems. The realization that a best friend has taken up with a new and wonderfully attractive young lover provokes envy rather than an analysis of why the friend feels the need to exchange his trusty old model for a new one. And, looking around, film stars, famous actors, politicians and well-known men the world over are photographed changing partners in their forties – so, most think, why not me too?

Therapists believe that the storm clouds start gathering when a man passes a mirror and instead of seeing a gilded youth reflected sees a man on the verge of middle age looking back at him. It confirms what he has begun to suspect: he is getting old. The face is a little more lined and fleshy, the hair less lustrous and the shape of the body, though still good, not quite what it was. Perfection seems to be inching further away. If he starts to reflect subconsciously he notices certain muscles ache and at night, it might be imagination, but his heart seems to have started to beat erratically. At his most vulnerable he wonders if his penis is less interested in its usual partner(s) than it used to be and what has happened to really stiff erections. Compounding the doubts the wife/lover starts commenting in public about their declining sex life.

From that moment the crisis starts, gathering strength on the downward slope. It is as if a slow fuse has been lit. He knows that unless he does something about it fast his life is going to deteriorate, fast. But what?

While the creeping physical slide due to the natural processes of aging makes him feel vulnerable, so the realization that unfulfilled ambitions are now never likely to be fulfilled sets up a panic. He sees himself locked into a lifestream that no longer satisfies his changing values and goals – at home and at work – and there is nothing he can do to make things better. Men with secure lifestyles and successful careers are affected, so too are men who, at the age of thirty-nine, realize they are too old to be in the running for promotion and too old to apply for the new jobs advertised.

Most men survive the traumas unscathed, if chastened, but some find the emotional upsets so painful and corrosive that though it does not drive them out of their minds it most certainly drives them into the arms of therapists, analysts and, if their egos are not too bruised, to new lovers.

Surviving the changes can be no easy matter but, let's face it, in his early forties a man's body is still in ripe condition to both give and enjoy pleasure and his mind far from addled by senility, so with the simplest adjustment, M-M can be tackled correctly.

Some, especially the men around forty you see jogging the hard city streets, take to sport as a positive way to prove lasting youthful vigour while others, equally youth-obsessed, prefer to rush around buying casual clothes from shops and boutiques that cater for the young crowd and start up lifestyles that gravitate around bars, discos, fast cars, jeeps and motorbikes. These men see their problems simply in terms of being *old.*

However, although exercise is beneficial, it is a solution that avoids the central issues and rushing around trying to pass for a young swinger is a short cut to disaster. To survive successfully and, indeed, to go into middle age successfully, requires mental adjustment to the future in terms of aims and ambitions. The male-menopause is the gateway to middle age. Instead of being on the fast lane with an all-out need to conquer, there must be a move on to a slower lane with a plan to aim for ideals that offer new and relaxing pleasures in life. For some a new job may prove the answer, or maybe a new marriage, but for most of us the solutions will be less dramatic. It is not a matter of opting out but of changing direction to something better.

The trick to survival is to spot what is good and make the best of it, whatever it is.

From the viewpoint of anyone currently in the grips of M-M it can seem that young people today have all the lucky breaks and that youth holds all the keys to the future. They do. As they have always done. But heed the words of a London therapist who swung mightily with the Swinging Sixties and is now a survivor in his late forties: '*Young people today do not appreciate what keys they hold any more than we did when we held them. But their time will come . . .*'

The Myths

Since the male-menopause has become a recognizable and diagnosable crisis condition many inaccurate theories and judgements have been circulated under the guise of being fact, each sounding like professional judgement from the pages of a medical textbook. This may not matter with simple ailments where a little embroidery improves the seriousness of tone and the quality of sympathy, but with the male-menopause all the myths do is increase misunderstandings and make less sense of what is potentially a serious matter.

Most popular myths centre on a man's sex life – or, more precisely, the apparent lack of it.

This may sound chauvinistic but many of the myths are probably put about by women. Not, one suspects, however, because of feminist need to establish equality but because to many women the term male-menopause conjures up visions of impotence and leads them to hope and expect men to have a similar sort of climacteric to theirs. After all if a woman has one why not a man too?

Perhaps the most important foundation to these myths comes from woman's knowledge of men. Looking around her circle and talking among wives it would seem that around their early forties men seek less sex with their regular partners and, if they are still able to perform fully in bed, then they are likely as not to go off the rails entirely chasing younger beauties, especially starlets, secretaries and air stewardesses. Many women see the male-menopause as either giving a man rampant sexual urges or stopping them altogether. On the whole they take more comfort from the latter.

The myths

SEX

a. *'Because of the male-menopause a man becomes impotent and either cannot get an erection or, when he does, cannot maintain one. He has no stamina left for sex.'*

fact: Not true. There is no hormonal or physical change during M-M so there is no change in either sexual urge or reproductive powers.

Should a partner find there is a lack of interest in sex she should first consider whether it is her own lovemaking that is no longer stimulating the man – that she might be sexually boring or stale. Or, is he enjoying his sex elsewhere?

b. *'If he is sexually highly active he will take on a young mistress.'*

fact: If he could, he would.

c. *'After the male-menopause a man is never again interested in sex.'*

fact: Not true.

d. *'When a man owns up to the fact that he has survived the male-menopause it means he no longer has an active sex life.'*

fact: Nonsense. Here is a man who understands and has survived the M-M crisis. He is probably indicating his sexlife has taken on a new dimension. He may also be sexually more adventurous.

e. *'He will have prostate problems.'*

fact: No. Not every man develops prostate gland problems and when they do it is usually after fifty-five as part of the inevitable decline due to aging. Younger than fifty-five, prostate problems are due to infection.

THE BODY

a. *'Male-menopause makes a man go bald.'*

fact: No. Whether a man loses his hair or not depends entirely on genetic inheritance and nothing more. Men inherit their hair pattern through either the maternal or paternal side of the family so it is a matter of luck whether they have a good head of hair. Both good heads of hair and baldness run through families. Nothing can be done to select which side you inherit from.

b. *'He will put on weight.'*

fact: He may do but it is entirely due to bad eating habits, not M-M. As we get older so, generally, we take less exercise and, as we therefore burn up less fat for energy, so we gain weight. To combat this tendency we should eat correctly – and less.

c. *'The male-menopause leads to heart problems.'*

fact: No. But men in their forties are prone to heart problems; it is the most lethal illness with one man in every four now aged thirty-five likely to be affected by the time he is sixty. With any unusual heart symptoms a doctor must always be consulted. Diet can play a beneficial part in keeping heart problems at bay: cut down consumption of all fatty foods, eat only lean meat and not much of it, use less salt and drink less caffeine (in tea, coffee and cola). Eat more vegetables and fruit.

HEALTH

a. *'He will get hot flushes and dizzy spells.'*

fact: No. If he does the cause is not M-M. He must consult his doctor.

b. *'He will let himself go physically and become a mess.'*

fact: He might. Surviving the male-menopause demands self-interest, self-respect, ambition. A man who lets himself go does so because his ego-balloon is punctured and he sees himself as a failure.

c. *'He will become emotionally unstable and unreliable.'*

fact: Perhaps. The male-menopause is essentially an emotional crisis.

d. *'Menopausal men take to drink.'*

fact: Many do but not all. Alcohol relaxes. It temporarily creates a feeling of wellbeing and in bars and at parties it helps create an illusion of still keeping up with the young set. It also temporarily blocks out worry and stress. Dependence on alcohol can become a major problem as a result of M-M.

e. *'Menopausal men take to drugs.'*

fact: Many do but not all. Drugs are often considered part of youth culture: many men believe that by joining in they are youthful too.

DRESSING-YOUNG

'All menopausal men start growing their hair long and buy clothes in styles meant for young men.'

fact: Many do, but not all. Although dressing-young is considered one of the signs of a man going through mid-life crisis not all men take to wearing clothes that look great on men in their twenties. Often they will go to the other extreme and take great pains never to buy any item they think looks young on them. However when a man in his forties starts togging up in fancy shirts, jewellery and has a fancy haircut and starts wearing tracksuits and designer label denim clothes to dinner and parties it is a sure sign that M-M has visited him. Mutton-dressed-as-lamb as the adage goes.

FLASHING

'Dirty old men who exhibit themselves to women and children in parks and other public places are going through the menopause.'

fact: No. Flashing is not an activity confined exclusively to menopausal men. Older men, boys in their teens and men in their twenties and thirties have been known to do it too. Some flashers may have the additional problems of M-M but their flaunting of the genitalia is a psychological problem, not one associated with M-M.

PACKAGING

'If you see a man with his genitalia laid out exhibitionistically down the front of one of his trouser legs you know he has menopausal problems.'

fact: Perhaps. Few M-M men exhibit themselves this way or think of doing so. This predilection is usually seen as a sign of aging with incidence higher among gay men than heterosexual. Many therapists in the United States believe that when a man of forty-plus starts dressing this way it is simply because he is worried about his declining sexual appeal and so believes by showing his prowess and availability all will be cured.

PART II

On what it is and how it affects you: the symptoms

What It Is

'If you find you are often depressed, bored, and irritable, that suddenly you hate your work, that you are suffering aches and pains, that you suspect you have a serious illness no one has diagnosed, that your sexlife is no longer what it was; brother, either you've got the male-menopause or you're over sixty.'

Therapist, New York.

In early stages of M-M certain outward signs show up and help identify the causes of the irrational feelings and behaviour of what appears to be, for many men, a curious decline in health. Of course many problems have their roots in diagnosable physical or mental conditions but for a man who until his early forties has been evidently healthy, with no signs of emotional instability, suffering from more than two of these obvious signs then it all adds up to the male-menopause.

No one incident or event triggers off the crisis. For some men the symptoms build up gradually over a period of months, maybe a year, while for others it is an overnight revelation. Either way, however, it is an irrational crisis that requires careful handling if people are not to be hurt or lives needlessly upset.

The crisis comes at a moment of transition, a time when a man still sees himself as young and has failed to notice that middle age beckons. He knows middle age is around the corner but his corner is some way off. One survivor says, on looking back, that he realizes now M-M was for him like being dragged across a mediaeval drawbridge into an enemy fortress called Middle Age. The problem was whether to capitulate and enter gracefully into the unknown or to resist and fight every inch of the way. (He fought.)

Until recently it was considered that the crisis struck a man soon after he was fifty but in this book all references are made to menopausal man being between thirty-nine and forty-five years. The reason for this change is tied in with the fact that men today achieve so much more earlier in their lives than ever they did before. Research by analysts and sociologists indicates that although some men may still experience the male-menopause late, with the more rapid growth of personal achievement and with expectations being fulfilled sooner – younger marriages, rewarding salaries, own home, work promotion – so the male-menopause strikes the majority of men earlier. Until recently where once a high-powered executive might have been fifty, now he is likely to be about forty if not younger. At fifty many men are already considered spent, overtaken by youthful men who have energy, push, skill, technology or invention on their side. The career ladder is climbed faster and faster. Although only partly concerned with the increased stress that ambition and fight for achievement bring, the male-menopause, like personal success, has also moved on to younger men.

In his early forties a man no longer passes for young but he is not old. Yet suddenly and somewhat unexpectedly it seems to him he is at a turning point where he is forced into facing up to himself and to the uncertainties of an aging future by taking stock of himself and re-evaluating all he finds. If his life is rich, full of interest and excitement, he can quickly take charge of his anxieties and move onwards. If it is dull he will invent diversion. If it is fraught with the competition of rat-pack work, his actions may be dramatic.

Not all symptoms affect each man the same way. Nor will personal reactions to the symptoms be the same.

At work, for example, a man in a bank with a steady and untaxing job may (perhaps rightly) complain about the constant boring and unchanging routine of his job while a man in an advertising agency where each job is different complains not of boredom but of the suspicion that his talent is no longer being fully appreciated and of being undermined by new creative people coming up on the outside lane. Their work problems are different but both subconsciously feel threatened, one by the endless boredom with its relentless routine ahead, the other by the worry about being spent creatively. Both would change jobs to totally different fields if they knew how.

And at home, after ten to fifteen years of marriage many feel trapped by a life over which they have no control. There are the responsibilities of mortgage, children's education, perhaps also aging parents. And then there is sex, or the lack of it.

By good fortune many men miss the male-menopause entirely because a lucky turn has taken place at exactly the right moment and given their lives the impetus and change other men with M-M are striving for. It could be a change of work that has saved them, maybe a promotion to a more interesting work field or, perhaps, a chance to move home to a better neighbourhood – anything that seems like a beneficial fresh start. Because, for all the references made to getting older, this is not essentially a quest for eternal youth. It is a crisis about change. Change and the chance of a fresh start.

A lament once voiced about different matters by novelist Edna O'Brien aptly sums up all a menopausal man asks at this time.

'All one wants from life,' she says, *'is a second chance. Isn't it?'* Exactly.

Since the problem was first correctly identified it has been known by a variety of names: *male-menopause, mid-life melancholia* and *middle-age anxiety* among them. Each title attempts to encapsulate in minimum words the long, irrational and emotionally disturbing period when a man wakes to the fact he needs to assess what and who he is, and what he expects from the future. At the moment of decision some shatter their lives with change while others come face to face with a realization that they are in no position to do anything even if they knew what it was they wanted. For this latter group the realization that dreams and expectations are destined never to be fulfilled, brings traumatic reaction. Egos plummet as they reach breaking point. The crisis starts.

Today the term *male-menopause* is universally accepted as useful because it neatly sums up the malaise. It sums up the general upheaval in life's continuity, a mid-life transition, rather than highlighting only one symptom. No term gives more valid reason why a man reaches this emotional crossroad with such a lust for change.

Of course as any man who has survived its rigours will admit, male-menopause is a fairly insulting term. Women in conversation laugh, and look quizzically at you if you own up to it. Surely you can't have had it already, they say, their deduction being you can no longer get an erection. And at home or at work women commonly enjoy the title if they can use it in connection with husbands or work colleagues because to them it implies, somewhat comfortingly, that a man is vulnerable and sexually on the skids – possibly at a time when they suspect their own menopausal decline is on its way. At a dinner table the subject gives them opportunity to fire barbs at their spouses, barbs to take them down a peg in everyone's estimation. A wife may be happier to accept the lack of sexual intercourse at home as being due to his menopause rather than face the possible fact that she no longer stimulates him sexually and offers him only, instead, companionship.

It is not unknown either for men to get mileage out of the title.

By publicly identifying the turbulence they attempt to get away with whatever self-indulgences they feel like, claiming that at this irrational time they are no longer responsible for their actions. A man will ignore his wife, girlfriend or family, spend extravagantly, buy a red sports car or jeep, chuck in his job and generally do what he wants to and blame it all on one thing, the male-menopause. For him it offers a built-in excuse: life is out of his control.

Unlike the woman's menopause which is due entirely to physical change within the body, the male-menopause comes about purely through emotional upheaval with the problems of having an aging body as an additional physical irritation. When evaluating life everything can appear in order – home, work, money, family, pets and acquisitions – yet the menopausal man is disturbed, unsure of himself, dissatisfied. Life is not what it should be and to make matters worse he notices he is getting old: wrinkles, less hair, backache, flabby waistline, bottom slung lower, possibly a need for reading glasses or an operation for varicose veins; all these going towards proving there is a physical decline he is powerless to prevent. And to top all this he may also find he has a less playful penis, a desire to live it up fast with a young set, a dependence on drink or drugs or other equally debilitating emotional problems that are ready to undermine his already fragile state.

The woman's menopause, her climacteric, is due purely to dramatic, internal change (although such a change invariably carries emotional side effects with it too). Medically, this menopause is defined as the cessation of menstruation brought on by the physiological failure of ovarian function due to hormonal changes caused by aging.

Throughout adolescence and the years of development, a woman's hormones, oestrogen and progesterone, affect her sexuality, appearance and temperament. After puberty their main role is to cause the thickening of the womb's lining each month in preparation for pregnancy which, if conception does not occur, leads to menstruation. However as she enters her fifties the production of oestrogen slows down and eventually ceases altogether. When it does she loses her reproductive powers and can no longer bear children. Menstruation ceases permanently. This menopause can take place over as long as five years.

Not all women experience the change the same way with exactly the same symptoms but for most this is an uncomfortable and traumatic time. Emotionally they can become irritable, depressed, weepy, forgetful, apprehensive and nervous or sexually demanding (similar symptoms can affect men during M-M). Physically they may suffer hot flushes and excessive perspiration. Breasts can shrink, hair become thinner, bones weaken and occasionally intercourse becomes uncomfortable due to loss of secretion. Sometimes there is a decrease in sexual responsiveness.

Supplements of oestrogen prescribed by a doctor can counteract most of these side effects and restore normality but they will not make a woman fertile again. After her menopause a woman loses the capacity to reproduce.

As men do not have a menstrual cycle nor a sudden cessation of hormone production the term male-menopause is used figuratively to allude only to a comparable decline in a man's life. But it is a psychological descent. Aging does not inevitably harm male potency and only after the mid-fifties is the production of testosterone in some men declining to any noticeable degree. However, it never reaches zero level.

Any serious loss of testosterone production found in men around forty is directly attributable to physical disfunction brought on by other causes, not the male-menopause. For them a short course of hormone therapy adjusts the imbalance.

It is not unknown however for some doctors in the United States to prescribe hormone injections as the antidote to M-M especially if their patients lay the blame for their current problems on a lack of sex drive or poor erection. But this is increasingly being regarded as wasteful treatment unless it has first been established decisively by clinical tests that hormone imbalance exists. If, as is most likely, the man's production of testosterone is normal, hormone injections are wasteful, and expensive. Many therapists make the charge that these doctors prescribe injections (where imbalance is not proved) because it is easier to apply a syringe than attempt by understanding and consultation to get a man through his menopause by bolstering or supporting his sagging emotional system. Injections they say do no more to cure the man than do the hundreds of Valium tablets supplied by other doctors.

Hormone injections however do have their uses and often a sexually active man in his sixties finds they boost his sexual energy effectively. These hormone injections also form part of geriatric therapy.

The basic problem of M-M concerns being able to begin again in the middle of life: how to get it right, how to be happy when the past looks richer than the future.

Many men at the height of their melancholia fight their crisis by making wild changes to their lives regardless of others' feelings and so hurt many people. And a considerable number of events or, indeed, scandals involving famous men or husbands in your own circle in the thirty-eight to forty-five age group can often be directly attributed (though not necessarily excused by) the wild actions brought on by M-M. One well-known London musician at this age consciously decided to shatter the existing structure of his life and went on to world fame with a new young wife with whom he started a second family.

But while some men see their solution in packing their bags, others, with what might be considered a more negative or pessimistic reaction, collapse in despondency to a depressed state of helplessness with a listless outlook on life and few interests apart from television and/or the bottle, their sex life not worth mentioning. Whatever the reaction, even though there may not be a vocal cry for help, somewhere along the line they are asking for help and understanding. It could be at home, in the office or in a doctor's consulting rooms.

It is unfortunate that a cry for help may not be recognized for what it is because not knowing how to come to the point and explain the troubles compounds a man's predicament.

Men are capable of a wide range of feelings and emotions yet somehow, possibly since history began, it is the accepted norm in masculine imagery to expect a man to hide his inner feelings. For a man, showing emotion appears to be equated with showing weakness – so asking directly for help to sort out what in essence is an emotional crisis takes an act of supreme bravery. Never before has he been more exposed or defenceless. Most, as a result, plump for complaining about their lot in the hope that someone will come to their aid with an easy solution.

According to therapists, looking for help at home represents the most difficult task. A wife will point out all that is good about his life (his job, his pension, his family, the car) and the reasons why he should not change anything (the mortgage, the pension, the money, school fees, aged parents). These are the very ties that are oppressing him but she sees them as his manly responsibilities. Her suggestions that *you pull yourself together* and *face up to your responsibilities,* although along the right lines, are hardly demonstrative of understanding or constructive in their support. She may also suspect because of his irrational behaviour that he is having an affair and suspect he is not telling her the truth anyway as he talks to her and that he is hiding something.

Confiding in a friend may be no more successful. He will probably point out how much better your life is than his and while baring the soul your anxieties, because they are impossible to explain logically, sound weak, unmasculine and silly. A man has to be very secure in his friendships to confide at such a time.

Talking to a doctor can be most help but he too will probably suggest *you must pull yourself together* and point out the innumerable advantages of your life. He may explain the symptoms of M-M and prescribe the short term solutions, tranquillizers and sleeping pills. He may recommend a psychiatrist if the depression is severe.

Of course everyone's values change with the passage of time so at forty you no longer crave the same things you wanted at twenty. What seemed vital in terms of money, position, promotion and security still matters but the emphasis has changed, you may not want so much. It can seem that old values and new ones have little in common.

What many people, women in particular, find difficult to accept is that a fully grown man well out of reach of adolescence can start showing all the apparently rootless signs of a college leaver or, worse, the unmasculine weaknesses never associated with successful mature men. And asking questions along the lines of *what can I do with my life?* and *what is there left ahead of me?* and making statements like *I feel trapped by my work and my life* or *surely this cannot be all there is in life for me* leads to condemnation not sympathy. When these anxieties are expressed by a man whose work and lifestyles have all the external trappings of success, the anxieties appear puerile and ridiculous. To aggravate matters further, if while asking the questions he is seen chasing girls (or young men), dressing young and boozing – or, being depressed and a boring misery to be with – all sympathy is stretched to its utmost and any wish to comprehend the problem blunted. After all, in our society every man is expected to know where he is going by the time he is forty unless he is emotionally hopeless or a failure. It is fine leaving college or university with doubts, but, at forty? At forty a man must have all his answers sorted out. Society *expects* him to know where he is going.

But can he?

The answer is no, if he is in the grips of the male-menopause he cannot. Being emotionally shaky is the nub of the menopause syndrome.

However in all reasonable honesty why should a man not have doubts and frustration as the curtain rises on the second half of his life? Why should he not crave new interests or excitement and want to satisfy new desires as increased maturity changes his ideas and needs? For all the outward signs of success or achievement he *is* on the threshold of middle age (considered these days to start at forty-five). Middle age demands a fresh outlook on life.

Nothing in the rule book states a man must not hope for a fresh start at forty with fresh goals and with a renewed appetite or enthusiasm for action, interest, development and most important, personal contentment. It is a turning point where priorities alter.

During the male-menopause as far as the M-M man is concerned it is time for action one way or another. For better or for worse.

How to recognize it in yourself — and others

a. The mental (downhill) slope
b. At work
c. At home
d. Health
e. On being young . . . or not

How to recognize M-M in yourself —and others

The symptoms of M-M cover wide territory that is both physical and emotional with no one symptom itself the signal beacon that says the male-menopause has started for this man. Many symptoms are serious and many, taken singly, are minor. Together they add up to the seemingly inevitable.

To the man who has it as much as the man who is observing a friend behaving erratically or oddly out of character, it should be some consolation to know that these disturbing symptoms linked together form part of a greater pattern that is likely to effect most men no matter how intellectual or full of commonsense they may be.

To the woman whose man is behaving irrationally the signs will show that this quirky behaviour is symptom and reaction to M-M and not simply due to excessive moodiness or mental instability. Nor is it confined to him alone.

In time M-M passes. But for a man to survive with style and success it demands positive action, willpower and know-how on his part, and from others, understanding, help or sympathy. Knowing the symptoms makes the spotting easier and paves the way for survival.

a. The mental (downhill) slope

The crisis builds up with a series of emotional upsets based on irrational doubts that, depending on each man's own reading of his life, spill out and apply equally to his home as well as work life. Serious or insubstantial, together they can rock a man's foundation. They can puncture his ego and undermine self-confidence. Self-esteem can be shot and sometimes there is a profound sense of failure which more often than not is unfounded and not evident to the eyes of others. For many the over-riding symptom is a feeling that they are missing out on their fair share of the joys of life (seen chiefly as sex). Other symptoms may be present too, nagging. Gradually the pressures intensify with tension, ragged nerves, a temper at the end of a short fuse the probable result.

And while some have only a small random selection to conquer, others have what appears to them to be more than their fair share for an inordinately long period. How badly it strikes depends entirely on personal make-up and environment. It may only be short-lived but therapists believe, at its worst, the male-menopause can last five years.

Change

> *'All I ask is a chance to change my life. I don't particularly want to get rich or have a mistress. That is fun but not a necessity. What I want is a chance to start again and be happy with my lot.'*
>
> Advertising executive, thirty-nine.

Some New York therapists refer to the desperate hankering for change that engulfs an M-M man as the *mid-life lust for change.* And just as the sense of failure can dog them, so many constantly view their future with a jaundiced eye at the prospect of a terrifying continuation of stale and meaningless years and feel impelled through self-preservation to break out at any cost and make a dramatic change to their lives.

From adolescence the future holds promise of continuous improvement. New experiences, greater expertise, more money, more sex, a wife, children, a home, promotion and once these are achieved, what next? At forty-plus?

Given half a chance most people at some moment of their lives would carry out change. But for menopausal men this yearning can become imperative need.

No two men will have exactly the same reaction but their self-doubts and questions at this time will run along the same lines: *what would make me happy and satisfied?* (in my eyes and those of my family and friends. Approbation is important at this juncture.) Not every man, for example, wants to swap his wife for a younger model or move house to a new locality and, although work is important for financial security and some succeed immeasurably by taking up different work, not every bored bank man wants to be a painter, nor every sculptor a travelling salesman nor every retail store executive a worker with missionary zeal at a charitable organization.

Nor does every man feel compelled to take a mistress, wear young clothes and take to drug culture, smoking pot and clamouring for coke.

If there is a common denominator in this search for change it is a need for fulfilment in a strictly personal way. It is aspiration to a change that will provide a degree of personal success through personal creativity. Being admired for individual ability. Only creative ability can supply satisfaction and answer the consuming need for mental stimulus and prevent the encroaching fear of being permanently bored. The urge is to be recognized for oneself rather than for being adept with things like figures, forward planning, administration, sales techniques or machinery.

For many men the solution may only require short term change but it is sufficient. Being able to handle a secret affair, for example, can for some answer their creative urge as well as sexual one. They see organizing and maintaining the affair in secret as creative ability and the affair itself a bonus proving their continuing sexual prowess. For an equal number taking a prolonged holiday helps, maybe with wide travel. In both cases although the change is not permanent it is stimulating enough to get them out of their rut so they can look on life refreshed. Many large companies today allow their executives to take a sabbatical for extensive travel, to write a book etc. This change recharges a valuable man's batteries.

The need for change can be urgent. For having discovered the solution to the problem many find not a second can be lost. Stale marriages are swept aside, dull jobs ended by penning a resignation letter. In a brave gesture of independence there might even be a fling to Paris or Acapulco with a young girl.

But making a true change cutting out of one lifestream and into another is not a move to be lightly taken and certainly not one for the weak. True change demands courage. Think of the consequences at home or at work while trying to explain the moves. Parents, friends, the boss, they only respect stability. To you stability may represent boredom, lack of initiative and enterprise or lassitude and dullness. To them one job, one family and a regular routine spells a nice guy with healthy understanding for responsibility. Wild gestures are never understood or condoned even if the move turns out to be shortlived before returning to the old life chastened and, maybe, revitalized.

To worry about the consequences is therefore realistic. Thinking before you jump, wise action. At forty there is no guarantee that any change is for the better or that success comes any more easily than it did at twenty-five. A man might be trapped in a dull job but handing in his resignation in times of recession without a new job to go to is highly risky and foolhardy. The sad fact is that fewer openings occur for men each year after thirty-five.

One London psychiatrist believes the issue of survival through change depends exclusively on a sense of personal identity.

'If a man knows who he is and is secure in his sense of identity he can affect his changes successfully and gradually re-establish himself. If his identity is only hazily sketched then the moment he steps out of his environment he is likely to sink. He will have to swim hard and long before he survives with any happiness or contentment.'

Failure

> *'The worst part of the male-menopause is the realization that your ambitions are hopeless. Your life is no longer on the fast lane on the highway. You are no longer twenty-five. Pulling over to the slow lane makes you feel a failure.'*
>
> Survivor, New York, forty-two.

The most damaging emotion in the crisis is sense of failure. Not that in tangible terms there has been or is about to be failure, but gnawing self-doubts start taking on major proportions and magnifying themselves beyond reason. A typical man facing up to M-M tries to conform to what society dictates and evaluates as its values and ideals. But when, as they do, his values change and his priorities are not those laid down by society, then he begins to suspect he is a failure. He cannot live up to what is expected of him. Even our archetypal successful man with flourishing business, comfortable homelife and respectable financial security can look around him and from his safe platform question his life, his very existence.

The gist of this problem has been summed up by a career journalist at the top of his tree with an international news magazine. *'I could see myself clearly. Good job, good life. But I thought, now what? I am forty-three, I have what I have, but is it what I want for the next twenty years? I took fright. I was trapped by a life I had created and could see no way of changing it. I was trapped . . . therefore I must be a failure.'*

To anyone standing on the sidelines and hearing such self-doubts expressed by an obviously mature and well-adjusted man, these improbable sentiments could seem foolish, frivolous or weak-minded nonsense. How can one participate in a conversation punctuated with *Is there nothing more ahead of me?'* or *'I am a failure, I have never achieved anything'* when the speaker is a healthy man about forty?

Most people's reaction is to tell the man to pull himself together and not to talk such nonsense – only someone with an understanding of the irrational babbling of a menopausal man looking for help can be the listening pillar of support he seeks.

Missing Out

Or feeling cheated

As part of the failure syndrome a man can see everyone in his circle as having a better life than he has whether in real terms they have or not. Everyone, he thinks, has a better home, car, travel, paintings and less responsibilities. And, more to the point, more fun. It is not that what he has is not good, but life, he feels, has only dealt him a poor hand of cards. He feels cheated and missing out.

For the largest percentage there is one area in which they all feel they are missing out – sex. As they see it they are simply not getting enough when compared with some friends they know and certainly, they are convinced, they are not getting their fair share.

These M-M men are invariably contented within their own worlds. Each has a steady job he enjoys, one with prospects and a substantial pension ahead, a wife or steady relationship he is happy with, a home and children to be proud of and a friendly social life that is as hectic as he would like it. They are never bored. By anyone's standards their lives look rosy and full of contentment.

Nonetheless when it comes to sex they feel they are missing out. All their men friends seem to be having a good time and having little flings on the side, so why not them too?

It is not that their sexlife at home is stale although probably it is more routine than adventurous but looking back they see and regret that in their earlier years they were not as wild or promiscuous as they could have been and certainly they never had as many sexual adventures or exploits as all their friends. An affair now will not affect their homelife; all they want is their fair share of fun. So, they look for affairs wherever they can. Mostly they are successful.

These are the men women worry about, the happily married men who manage to cheat and enjoy a secret love life and still go home to bed with their wives.

'What she doesn't know, doesn't hurt her. For all I know she is having an affair while the kids are at school in the afternoons. Listen, at my age why shouldn't I have an affair? It means nothing. An affair makes you feel good.'

Accountant, forty-four, London.

Aggression

Because of frustration with himself and with his life a subconscious internal fury can build up and belligerence become a serious problem. For no reason tempers can fray and if the fists don't fly, certainly the tongue does the lashing. Short temper and poor tolerance become the norm. Pedestrians in the way on a sidewalk, shop assistants, bank tellers, waiters, barmen and people generally supplying a service catch the brunt of the raging ire. Bad service can bring violent displays of temper to the surface.

During M-M a normally calm and pleasant man can turn almost overnight into an intolerant, short-tempered person. Psychiatrists explain this as aggression brought on entirely due to a man's frustrations with himself. As his life evens out so his tolerance will return to normal and his temper back to its original state.

The Complaint Syndrome

Because life seems to be taking on a negative form, almost every aspect of it seems wrong and requires deploring verbally at every opportunity. There is a relentless need to complain about anything impinging on his life whether major or minor. Sometimes he will complain with good reason – about noise, the neighbour's children, television programmes – but mostly the complaints are far reaching taking in every aspect of his daily life. He has little good to say about his children, family, home cooking, restaurants, holidays, public transport, money. Mention a subject and he will find a point to complain about. Refer to his work and he will tell of his resentfulness to its rat-race qualities, how he has poor reward or appreciation and if it were not for family responsibilities how quickly he would chuck it all in.

He is no longer fun to be with.

Irritability

Because of his discontentment with his lot a menopausal man's temper is often on a short fuse. He behaves in an irritable manner, his temper flaring up at the smallest provocation. The irritability is irrational and unintentional. Bad moods may last many hours. See *Aggression.*

Best defensive action is to avoid him as he will take out his temper tantrum on anyone near him. If however you are the man in question, take yourself away. Go for a walk, take in a movie. Enjoy the solitude of your own company until the irrational irritability passes.

Life Panic

Waking alert at 3 a.m. and not being able to sleep again is an unpleasant experience for anyone but waking with anxieties based on self-doubt flooding the mind and with an imagination capable only of seeing gloom, this is like living a wide-awake nightmare. Panic sets in, life has never looked so bad.

An image of failure, a sense of futility, the lack of opportunity for further personal fulfilment, problems with sex, money or work, all loom large in the imagination and become abundantly clear matters for anxiety. In the darkest hours the troubles are at their blackest. And swampingly depressing. Life panic is bleak.

Some men find a book helps concentrate their minds on other things or get out of bed to avoid lying in despair. As the male-menopause resolves itself so the waking problem diminishes and sleep patterns return to normal. Until then life panic magnifies.

It has been observed that too much alcohol late at night can spark off life panic. Whether this is due to waking in order to urinate then being unable to sleep or whether excessive alcohol stimulates mental uncertainty is not clear, but alcohol does, in its short term, make a man feel buoyant, slowing down his nervous system and inducing a feeling of happiness through lessened worry and inhibitions. He thinks less clearly and physical action slows down. At night, however, when the soporific effects have worn off and with a slowed down system reality can be hard to bear. Anxieties appear clearer and more oppressive.

Religious Rebirth

> *'I need God. I never did before but now I need to know someone is there, someone I can talk to and lean on who will take care of me. I need help.'*
>
> Writer, forty-two, London.

Looking for comfort and solace, many men turn to religion. If they come from families already steeped in religion or have had childhoods where the family attended Sunday service they may return to practising their own faith becoming what is currently termed born-again-Christians. But many in experiment and seeking deeper involvement and spiritual experience turn to Catholicism seeing it as a spiritually demanding faith, or to the lesser known mystical religions like Sufism, prepared to attend class and study the new faith as they embrace it.

In his observations a London analyst concludes that whereas one might cynically accuse old people who in their last years turn to religion of doing so from superstition, preparing for heaven rather than hell, menopausal men turn to religion purely for the emotional pillar and support it affords them. Renewed faith assists them through life. In their prayers they ask for help, indulgence, direction and generosity that they might sort out the muddle of their lives and fulfil life's obligations satisfactorily and, if possible, to turn their lives to better use. To change. Faith gives a feeling that in some secure way their lives are being protected. Without God's help they feel impotent about effecting change.

Many men will try to bring their family to their renewed faith but many will see it as a strictly private involvement preferring to practise without comment from other persons.

As the act of praying is essentially personal, one of the special comforts of faith is that prayers can be said privately at any time without necessarily visiting a place of worship. Communication and meditation is secret.

'I always pray on the bus going to and from work,' says a survivor, *'and when walking the dog. It is the only time when I can feel totally alone. For me a really good few minutes of praying has a far better calming and comforting effect than two glasses of vodka ever did.'*

b. At work

> *'Some men sink to the bottom when they make changes, others flourish. This is particularly true with work. What helps achieve success is the ability to aim realistically and to keep future expectations within the realms of reality.'*
>
> Psychoanalyst, London.

At work a man in the grips of the male-menopause fluctuates between feeling unappreciated for his talent and effort, and, feeling physically spent with little energy in reserve, resentful at being what he considers to be over-burdened with too heavy a workload. He may be bored by the endless quality of the job or worried that his creative ability is not matching up to the demands imposed on him. And, in most cases, he will also believe that the management is hopeless, inefficient and greedy while he considers the new up-and-coming group around him pushy, sycophantic and dangerous. He is even suspicious of long-term colleagues.

He also feels trapped. Even at the top of a successful career ladder and with a solid and secure company behind him he can feel trapped in his business world with a future offering no promise.

At the age of forty-plus and with at least twenty working years ahead, work has become a drudge. He wants change. He feels trapped by circumstances and hates himself for blindly getting himself into such a predicament.

For most men the rungs on the work ladder are obvious, each step clearly defined. With an equal amount of ability, flair, work achievement and luck the ladder can be steadily climbed. But for a man around forty the work world has shrunk. Promotion is harder to come by, the opportunities less. In fact, from thirty-five onwards opportunities within a company thin out and the possibility of switching to, or finding, work with stimulating or interesting prospects, equally rare. Something must be done.

In an effort to prove their worth, as much to themselves as to others, some take on excessive work loads. They need to impress. They work late, take paperwork home, work weekends. They are prone to stress and heart attacks.

Others, feeling burnt-out creatively, want out. Out of their stream and into another. This is particularly a reaction of men in the arts fields where ideas and the ability to follow-through are vital. It is not that at forty the body is too old (as it may be becoming in dance and the sports fields, for example). It is not. But, in the competitive fields of advertising, movies, journalism and theatre where mental creative follow-through is important people may see the man as having an output verging on brilliant while inside he fears he is burnt-out and able to get no further than putting the subject title on paper. His mind he feels is tired and has lost its nimbleness and facility to surprise. Therefore he wants out and into a new work field where success cannot be judged or compared to past skill or past fame.

For many men the mere suspicion that failure is ahead makes it imperative they get out of their stream and into something new and personally satisfying. They may run down their work so that their output becomes regarded as useless and perhaps subconsciously they hope to be dismissed so that the final act of severence is in someone else's hands. Many will throw up a career or profession as if this original line of work is of no importance.

The moment of realization that they are not only disillusioned with their work but also disappointed with themselves can be chastening. Nothing seems to go right, work least of all. Their career has come to a halt and work represents hell. Life, it seems, has them trapped unfairly. As one survivor, an ex-gynaecologist now running an art gallery in Italy, sums up this moment: *'I thought surely there must be more to life than this job, retirement and death.'*

With sympathetic help and understanding an M-M man can at this point shake off the sense of defeat or revise his ambitions and priorities. Perhaps he can be encouraged to realize a life's dream of moving to the country to open a bookstore, for example, or to the coast and owning a boat. Without help at this moment the risk is a man can become a middle-aged dropout – and there are many of those to be seen in countries where the cost of living is low, the sun high and the drink cheap.

> *'The decision to resign a job must be made with some maturity and with a realistic understanding of present day opportunities. His decision must be based on personal strength and his ability to survive change, not made rashly from boredom or as an escape from responsibility.*
>
> *'For success all future expectation must be reasonable. Men who take stock of what they have and see they can inject new activities into their home life with more sport, hobbies, travel or weekend trips invariably do better than the man who walks out of his office thinking "to hell with them all" and expecting that only by doing something dramatic will he come up trumps.'*
>
> Therapist, London.

c. At home

At home there are two routes: either he becomes out of sorts, listless and dull to be with, or, he becomes diametrically the opposite, energized, full of vitality, a partygoer, king of the nightlife.

In both instances although he values the security of home he feels trapped by it and in private moments fantasizes how life might have been had he not so hastily married.

As for his sex life – see *Sex: No-Go or Go-Go* (page 47).

Listless

He wanders about bored, beating a regular path to the kitchen to raid the refrigerator for a little snack. He complains of feeling tired and wants to go to bed earlier each day, rarely much after 9.30 p.m. Household repairs if ever started are never completed. He feels ill.

Energized

There is a frantic burst of energy and an intense need for social activity and late nights. But not at home.

Breaking away from the comfortable and companionable pattern of recent years, under the banner of personal freedom he suddenly starts going out with the boys from the office or club. Pubs, bars and even office or club events become the focal part of his life, anything rather than come straight home from work to the secure homelife that he now finds claustrophobic with responsibilities weighing heavily around his neck. He will also consider taking up sport: jogging, squash, workouts at the gym. Men in their early forties jogging the urban streets epitomize the fighting and surviving menopausal man.

Indecision

The attitude is that nothing seems to matter any more. Nothing appears important enough to justify his making a decision even if it is as simple and homely as which movie to see or whether to cook spaghetti at home or eat Chinese take-out. *You choose, it doesn't matter* becomes the catch phrase.

Emotionally depressed, few practical decisions can be made. The menopausal man prefers to rely on others for their advice and their decision. He is floundering and trying to sort out his own muddled existence. Compared to the self-doubts fermenting within him these day-to-day decisions can seem trivial. He is difficult to be with.

Boredom and Fatigue

If he is not bored with everything about him he is tired. And during M-M fatigue and boredom go hand in hand. Fatigue leads to boredom, boredom to fatigue. And increased lethargy. The more he slows down his pace and narrows his interests seeing his life through grey-tinted specs the more bored he becomes. Inertia is inevitable.

Regenerating his interests with new or different activities is a solution where both family and friends can be helpful but trying to stimulate his enthusiasm will be an up-hill struggle. Without great effort on his part these symptoms become chronic – and then the menopausal man has good reason for feeling sorry for himself.

Restlessness

In direct contrast to the men in the fatigue syndrome, some men swing to the opposite extreme of constant activity as if terrified of being bored or set in sedentary ways. They are constantly on the move.

This is not productive activity however, simply restlessness. They will watch a football game on television for a few minutes, get up, take a walk in the garden, visit the kitchen for a quick snack, pick up a magazine, return to television and run through a gamut of activities that are neither productive nor restful. Household chores if started are never finished. They complain of being bored.

Their restlessness makes them disturbing company.

Daydreaming

Escapism. From an early age everyone daydreams. It is a free, personal, easy and secret way of escaping reality. Daydreams are happy and always improve the quality of life as they feed the fantasy. And an M-M man uses them too to pretend he is improving his lot. He may be driving the car, walking to the subway, sitting at his work or even relaxing in an armchair and his mind will have wandered into another world where life is at its best, perhaps with some glamour, more sex, a new job, new house, money or, simply, escape. Reality has little to do with the dreams; these are fantasies about how life could be if only . . .

Returning to reality may make the reality seem worse. Feeling resentful he may vent his aggression on those nearest him.

Daydreams only occasionally offer practical solutions to problems.

Family Feuding

Tied in with the belligerence borne of frustration, a man can goad his family or even his friends into a sniping war by his ill-temper. Children against parents, each individual against the other. Wives are alienated, grandparents shaken, best friends upset; marriages break and lovers are lost all because inner frustration is driving the man into irrational, fighting mood. Words sting.

Irreparable damage can be done. Apologies are hard to come by and insufficient.

Self-questioning

Now what? Essentially a part of his fears of failure, he sees a need to question every motive and every move. No part of his life feels like a success no matter how family or friends try to prove that it is. He wants to achieve more but he does not know what it is he wants. When he makes a decision he is always plagued with the doubts: *is it worth it?* and *why should I bother?*

As he doubts himself he questions his worth. He can be very gloomy to be with.

Being Healthy

The onset of M-M can make a man more aware of his health than ever he has been before and being fit can become a major preoccupation. Being fit offers hope of retaining youth if not recapturing it.

The most concerned react energetically by taking to jogging, playing the occasional game of squash, watching their weight and eating a diet low in fat and carbohydrate, and purchasing vitamin pills in bulk.

Some with a leaning towards the aesthetic concentrate on the inner man, giving up alcohol and tobacco and turning to vegetarianism and healthfood store products for their salvation, while those with a leaning towards hypochondria head for their doctor's consulting rooms.

Those taking regular exercise and eating a balanced, sensible diet find they feel better and life generally looks better.

Hypochondria

Feeling sorry for himself and begging all kinds of love, care and attention, the M-M man constantly feels under par with each week producing a new and different symptom, each one building up a worrying pattern that results in a deep suspicion that something potentially serious might be taking place internally. The body seems slowly to be falling to pieces, something must be wrong.

It may be due to aging, he might sometimes think, but what if it is an undiagnosed creeping illness? Cancer maybe, or liver disease, kidney failure or diabetes. Eventually he will be driven to visit his doctor with a long list of small ills common to most M-M men at some time. Among them blinding headaches, pains in the eyes, nausea, flatulence, chronic fatigue, listlessness, hangovers, stomach pains, back-ache, sore joints and hot flushes. His eyesight for reading is not quite what it was; he blames modern lighting.

It is quite likely that he will also hear his heart beating erratically at night and get painful palpitations and as he worries more about them so the symptoms will heighten. At this age heart problems affect a large percentage of men so, imagination or not, he should visit his doctor. See *Health* page 35.

Alcoholism

Drink problems often increase with job achievement on the way to the top. Drink can help boost confidence or rejuvenate behaviour (called loosening-up in this context). For many menopausal men this is the start of alcohol dependence and only by drinking can they get themselves through a working or vitally social day.

The London Alcoholics Anonymous believe men turn to alcohol to help achieve work targets they set themselves and so achieve promotion and then, in their early forties, because they see no way upward on the promotional ladder, turn to drink to bolster their egos.

More than five drinks a day is regarded as serious rather than social drinking.

Divorce

> *'When we met we were both forty. My marriage was over but his was a daily trial without a future. Now he has shed twelve pounds, looks great and his career is on the up. We have fun, we travel and the six children we have between us get on fabulously.'*
>
> Diana, survivor's second wife, London.

It has been observed by some sociologists that the rate of divorce around the forty age group is inordinately high in percentage terms when compared with other age groups. Of course this is not due exclusively to the male-menopause but the male-menopause may well have a lot to do with it. Divorce is just one of the many reactions of M-M men as they seek change.

By this age both husband and wife will have developed strong, individual values and if they married when between twenty and twenty-five, now around fifteen years later, there is no reason why they should have matured along the same lines. Some will have naturally grown closer together but many will have developed different values and needs compared to those of their earlier years. Sexlife may have become routine, spasmodic and not very exciting.

Although there is no statistical proof, through observation it has been concluded that at this age menopausal men seek divorce in order to start again, specifically, to remarry. (The majority of non-menopausal men divorcing seem to prefer to enjoy their new found freedom rather than remarry at the earliest opportunity.)

When a menopausal man changes wife, his wife falls usually into one of two categories. Either she is young and attractive or she is ambitious with a strong personality.

Younger wives are usually sexy, probably more than ten years younger than the husband. Apart from a revived sex life they bring him the chance of being reborn, a young family, renewed pride (at having the young wife) and, as important, a wife who will cushion his life as she looks after him.

Strong wives are wives with push, ambition and loads of personality. Often they are highly attractive too. There may be little age difference between husband and wife and these are wives who see the unfulfilled potential of the husband's work and so inject into him the extra ambition he needs to get ahead, for more goals in life. They are supportive and whenever they can will try to further his career and promotion by participating in the social aspects of his worklife.

Once an M-M man has decided on packing his bags and leaving the marital home – he is the one who leaves – there is not much a wife can do. The options are in his hands.

Should she love him still and want him back, or, as is likely, she wants him back if only to make him face up to his responsibilities (like bringing up the children), the only course is to hope he comes to his senses and returns. Any action she takes is likely to alienate him further and disturb her even more.

If the marriage is stale and she does not mind him leaving, probably on the terms she dictates, then once the recriminations are over a friendship can be made out of the debris.

Keeping Up (with the boys)

> *'It really does not seem possible . . . my husband is trying to live our son's life; to have his fun at weekends, his parties, his sport and even his kind of clothes. He either struggles to join him or to compete. For heaven's sakes! Our son is only sixteen!'*
>
> Wife, London.

It is not unusual for some men to look at their son's youth and lifestyle and envy it for its apparently care-free freedom. Just as opportunities are shrinking in their own world so the son's are growing.

They do not begrudge the son his pleasures and take pride in being able to provide for all the family but, like the man who feels he is missing out on life, many have emotions tinged with envy as they see limitless opportunity ahead of the son.

Perhaps seeing the son enjoying himself signals the passing of youth because for some M-M men this becomes a time of reckoning. They take stock of themselves and re-appraise their appearance. They diet, take care about the way they dress and consider a new barber and contact lenses instead of spectacles. By being constructive life improves. The family approve and appreciate the change.

In keeping up, others involve themselves in their son's activities as diverse as going camping with the gang or taking up pot-holing or canoeing. For many this is a great pleasure especially if father and son are close and have enjoyed a sporting kindredship since the boy's childhood. However a number of fathers find that it is only when nearing forty that fitness and sport become important and many sons at this point resent what they see as their fathers' intrusion into their lives.

And while they may admire the son's effortless ability to have a life full of fun, a number will desperately demand acknowledgement from the son for the great generosity they are bestowing on him. (This is not a reaction exclusive to menopausal men.) As a result some are unnecessarily strict with the son. Family disagreements can be vociferous especially if there are younger children within the family to be compared with, children who because of their age are more docile and stay-at-home. This can be a trying time until the M-M father accepts his son's youthful need for adventure, experiment and independence.

'It is quite natural for the father to look at his son and envy him his life but he should also take pride in knowing that it is he, the father, who has made it all possible for the son,' says a London therapist.

'He should not expect gratitude as his due, however. How many sons say thank-you to their parents even if they should?'

d. Health: the physical recession

> *'By forty I thought I had gotten past it. For months I had felt depressed and discontented with everything . . . but nothing more. I still looked good with a tan on the beach.*
>
> *'Then at forty-five my world fell apart. I felt suicidal and my body behaved like someone else's, not mine. Now THAT was the male-menopause!'*
>
> Survivor, forty-seven, L.A.

Despite the myths and rumours, there are no purely physical symptoms that can be directly attributed to the male-menopause. There are, as we know, no hormonal changes to take place but there are strange side effects, both real and imaginery, that can be triggered by it nonetheless. Many are linked with the problems of having an aging body to contend with.

Playful Penis

Or to be more precise, the non-playful penis.

For many men this is the only obvious side effect they worry about, the side effect that makes them fear for the future.

As sex looms so large as a potential problem during the male-menopause it is considered separately. See *Sex: Go-Go or No-Go* (page 47).

Night-Rising

That is, getting up at night to pass water. (See also *Life Panic* page 26.)

Night-rising is one of the early warning signs of prostate problems so when a man becomes aware of just how often he is jumping out of bed at night to pass water he can, understandably, become alarmed. But most menopausal men need not worry. Unless he has caught an infection he is unlikely to be affected. Prostate problems *if* they do occur, affect men from their late fifties onwards.

The need to pass water once or more times at night comes simply from drinking too much late in the evening or last thing at night as a nightcap. Alcohol, tea or coffee. At M-M time most men increase their alcohol consumption in the evenings, especially wine. It is therapeutic, relaxing and makes them feel good. However, wine, like tea, has diuretic qualities which means it stimulates the production of urine and hence the need to urinate. It also causes dehydration because the body urinates more liquid than it takes in so thirst rages to make up for the loss. The answer is to control the amount you drink at night or adjust to the fact that night-rising is now part of life's pattern.

Drug Dependence

Both on pills and the harder stuff.

Whereas only a few mature men ape the youth drug culture with its uppers and downers, poppers, pills, speed and heroin, a considerable number cling to the social world coloured by marijuana and coke thinking it makes them youthful, liberated, fun and in touch. Yet more live in a world dependent on pills – anything from analgesic purchased from a supermarket or pharmacy to tranquillizers like Valium over-prescribed by some doctors as the panacea of all ills.

Drug and pill dependence is not a problem confined only to men during the male-menopause. It requires a secure and mature mind to throw off the dependency.

Night Sweats

Waking in the night bathed in sweat, hot or cold, anxieties flooding the imagination, is a physical side-effect of *Life Panic.* Unpleasant and uncomfortable, it passes as the menopause does.

Heart Problems

At around forty the body develops its first internal signs of aging. The external ones are already in position – wrinkles, crepy skin and baggy eyes – but now the internal problems make themselves apparent. The most disturbing often concerns the heart. An inordinately high number of deaths in this age group are due to heart attacks. See *Aging* and the heart (page 41).

Because one of the effects of M-M is to make a man vulnerable and doubt his own strength both emotionally and physically, many suspect they have the makings of a weak heart and wake every night listening to erratic heart beats, palpitations and fibrillation. For many this is just part of the M-M syndrome that encourages a vivid and panicky imagination but, as with most physical problems, every man should consult his doctor nonetheless if only for the consolation of hearing nothing is wrong.

High blood pressure may develop at this time due to stress and hypertension.

It is not unusual for a doctor to suggest checking the blood's cholesterol count by taking a blood sample. High cholesterol and heart problems are linked because cholesterol blocks the veins and so forces the heart to tax itself as it works harder to pump sufficient blood through the system to where it is needed. A fat-free diet can help return cholesterol levels to an acceptable count.

Hangovers

It is a curious phenomenon that men can have worse hangovers during the male-menopause than at any other time in their lives. Whether this is simply due to the fact they drink more alcohol during this period than at any other time is not clear. Some swear to having as severe a hangover with only two glasses of white wine as they do after a night out with lashings of iced vodka and lavish amounts of red wine at dinner.

Perhaps man's disturbed emotional system causes the body to burn up alcohol at a different rate or perhaps because drinking is more important they are not eating enough. Food will buffer alcohol; alcohol consumed on an empty stomach has quicker and greater effect and is more likely to lead to a hangover.

e. Aging: the truth

After thirty-five the body is not quite what it was. It may look passable in the mirror but compare it with another ten to fifteen years younger and the differences show.

In your twenties you look young and full of go. In your thirties you reach a peak with a kind of free sophistication and confidence. But in your forties?

The answer is that in your forties you have reached both a plateau and a turning point but if you have taken care of yourself and the way you look, you can still look your best with a distinguishing touch of maturity. It is by no accident that famous movie stars reach their forties looking good; they have taken intensive care.

But, and this is an emphatic but, at forty there is also a realization or revelation that maturity might not be all it is cracked up to be and that not only do you look mature with your thickening waistline and fuller face but that you also begin to *feel* mature. Both mentally and physically. People around seem to be just that touch younger than you. And meanwhile your values are changing, at work, home, leisure and generally. Time you realize is flying and the moment has come to lay foundation for future contentment; positive changes before it is too late.

For all of us, from the age of twenty it is downhill all the way. It is a fact, unless we are taken off by an accident or serious illness, instead of dying at our peak (in terms of looks, fitness and ability), when we breathe our last our bodies are in an advancing state of decay and collapse. Perhaps the Great Creator has it wrong. It would have been kinder and more enjoyable if our lives moved on an upward curve so that we popped off to the next world at a high peak rather than fade out exhausted at the end of a long run, our faculties worn out. However, that is how it is. The route unchangeable. Although some of us weather the years better than others, from the age of twenty our bodies are programmed to age.

All is not lost of course. If growing old is inevitable, feeling irreconcilably old is not. If a wise man in his thirties keeps his body rich in strength, energy and sexual drive, by his forties he should still be able to consider himself a good specimen even if the edges look slightly tarnished. Fortunately the changes come slowly and recent studies show that if you get to seventy in good condition then you have another twelve to twenty years ahead of you yet.

Not all of us mature in the same way; some age quickly, others slowly. Those who do better usually have genetics on their side (they come from a long-lived family) or do better simply because in their early years they have taken elementary precautions. Any man who in his early twenties starts taking care of himself with healthy eating habits, exercise and skin grooming will certainly fare better than the man who takes no care at all and indulges in tobacco, alcohol, drugs and so-called mind-enhancing substances, all of which in time ravage the body inside and out.

As our bodies age, the heart, lungs and muscles weaken generally – but within the time span of youth and M-M this deterioration should be suspected rather than obvious. Muscles get weaker, the body becomes stiffer, it is slower to heal if injured. It is good insurance during the thirties to take some form of regular exercise in order to keep the total body and its workings in trim. For most men two forty-minute workouts a week are ideal or a twenty-minute swim three times a week excellent. If this regular pattern continues into the forties and fifties there is nothing to be lost and all to be gained. The body will be at its best.

But . . . it will still age.

First, the Bad News

Head

At thirty the forehead is wrinkled, laughlines are lightly distinguishable around the eyes. This is character.

At forty the bags under the eyes are more pronounced, eyelids develop heavier folds, wrinkles etch deeper. This is also character. The face can also look as if the man is putting on weight as lines start to appear on either side of the mouth running down the face leading to a spare fold of flesh under the chin. The foundations of a permanent double-chin show. A fold of fleshy skin appears in front of the ears.

What has happened is that with age the natural powers of water retention under the skin have started to weaken, retention that was essential to the skin's elasticity and its ability to spring back constantly into shape. Now it stretches, sags and wrinkles and no matter what claims are made by product advertising, no amount of wrinkle cream will remove wrinkles, nor eyecream remove puffy bags any more than moisturizers can feed moisture back into the skin by being rubbed into it. Cream cannot nourish or feed moisture into the skin, it simply covers it.

However if after a wash or shave the skin feels taut a moisturizer will ease and soften the surface of the skin. And make it look better and healthier. A suntan will add aesthetic appeal.

During the thirties and forties hair thins out so if there is a baldness pattern running in the family it will make itself evident. The hairline will recede at the temples, the crown might thin or turn to a bare patch. MHB, that is Male Hereditary Baldness, governs just how good a head of hair you have. Each of us inherits a pattern through the side of the family that is genetically dominant – in the way we might inherit the family nose, colouring or body shape. What you get is a matter of luck and nothing can be done to change your inheritance.

As yet there is no proven miracle cure for baldness, certainly not one that can be medically substantiated. Massage and intensive courses of vitamins can make for a healthy scalp and improve the condition of the hair that remains but it cannot make hair grow again once the roots are dead and growth has stopped. Transplanting and the surgical tightening of the crown have limited success.

In the forties hair also begins to lose its colour and grey hairs flourish in large numbers. In reality these hairs are not grey but colourless as, due to aging, the production of pigmentation has slowed down (eventually to stop altogether) and individual hairs have become colourless. Mixed in with hairs still coloured the colourless hairs appear grey; as soon as every hair loses its pigmentation the head of hair appears white. Some of us change colour sooner than others and without dye there is no way of re-activating or restoring the hairs' colour. Aging kills off the power to produce hair pigment.

Curiously enough although many men go bald as they age, so they also get hairier. But not on the head. Eyebrows start to grow, hairs shoot out of the nostrils and ears. All three should be trimmed if a man is going to look his best – and younger. Hair protruding from ears and nose is universally regarded as a sign of age.

Teeth

Tooth decay is caused by eating highly refined foods and sweets and by poor dental care. By the time a man nears forty the protective enamel covering of the surface of each tooth will have worn thinner and the layer of dentin beneath become translucent. The teeth will require more care and more careful cleaning.

Gum infection, again due to diet and poor care, may become a problem too, attacking the roots of the teeth or causing gums to shrink and recede. For many men receding gums become a major problem at forty. The average man of this age will have five teeth missing.

It is fortunate for us that dentists can repair much of the damage and improve the appearance of teeth using mixtures of capping, bonding and bridging and with special gum treatments or surgery. With regular dental inspections and correct daily oral hygiene further deterioration can be prevented.

Seeing and Hearing

Eyesight declines during the thirties and by the time they reach forty most men have difficulty identifying fine print and need a strong light to read by. Most men prefer to blame the poor lighting rather than admit a need for spectacles. They may also have difficulty with night vision and driving in the dark.

The reason for this decline is that the eye's lenses harden with age so altering the focal vision. By the age of fifty it is inevitable that a hefty percentage of men will require reading glasses.

On the plus side, some men who have worn glasses since childhood may find their eyesight improved. Not much, but better. Hardening of the lenses sometimes partially corrects nearsight.

As for hearing, the older we get the less we actually hear or differentiate between high-pitched notes. Fortunately the deterioration is slow and deafness neither imminent nor inevitable. Few of us need to hear or identify high-pitched notes and at forty, because of changing values and interests, silence, peace and quiet, become additional valuable commodities. At forty though hearing loss makes a man aware of aging, it seems a relatively unimportant change.

Height and Weight

Not only do we put on weight as we age, we shrink.

At thirty a man is at his tallest but as muscles weaken through lack of exercise so his posture stoops, he no longer stands erect. And, the cushions between the bones of the spine wear thin. In the forties he will shrink a sixth of an inch, by the time he is sixty he will have lost over three-quarters of an inch.

But while he shrinks he also puts on weight. The reason is, simply, fat.

It is a sad fact that just when food becomes one of the major pleasures of life so we should be cutting down on the amount we eat. And drink (alcohol).

The older we get, the less exercise we take. The less we exercise, the less fat we burn up for energy so the more we put on weight – mostly around the waistline with fatter stomach and thicker hips. At forty we should be eating less quantity and less rich foods than we did in our twenties. On average most men put on seven to ten pounds between the ages of thirty and forty. Many doctors believe that unless a man was already overweight at thirty this is the weight he should aim to keep for the rest of his life.

Too much good food and drink and not enough exercise result in one thing: fat.

The Heart

During a man's forties heart problems, both real and imaginary, start taking shape. A large number of men will have all the symptoms of something wrong and have a check-up only to find nothing is.

However, heart disease does account for a high percentage of deaths in the forty-plus age group.

In Britain it has been estimated that one man in four will have coronary disease before he is sixty and one man in ten will die from it. Fortunately it has also been calculated that at least fifty per cent of men who go to their doctors complaining of heart pains have, in reality, chest pains caused not by heart disease but by stress and anxiety – so there could be good news waiting not just bad.

(Stress is today regarded a major factor in the cause of heart disease. However it is being suggested that doctors may have over-emphasized its effects as stress produces its own additional subconscious hypochondria and manifests itself, in particular, in all the symptoms of heart disease in an otherwise healthy heart.)

The reason for such an unhealthy decline at this age is that the heart muscles, like the body itself, are weakening with age and in its deterioration its pumping action has become less efficient so that it has to strain in order to supply the body with the circulating blood it needs. Eating fatty foods and smoking tobacco will have helped put it further out of condition by adding a blood pressure problem that forces the heart to strain further.

For some undiscovered reason, although the aging process affects men and women equally, heart problems affect women less. Doctors currently believe this is due to the daily stress and tension on a man brought about by the constant cut and thrust of pressures of work and the demands of being the backbone to the family. It is also estimated that many more men smoke tobacco than do women and men invariably have higher cholesterol levels in the blood – both of which are recognized causative factors of heart conditions. (Where men score over women is the face. A man's skin dries out less quickly than a woman's so he ages better.)

At thirty a healthy heart will pump about 3.4 litres of blood a minute and during exercise the beat will rise from seventy a minute to about 180 to 200.

At forty the same heart will pump about 3.25 litres a minute and during exercise the beat will rise only to 160 to 180 beats a minute.

By the time he is sixty both these figures will have further declined. The heart will pump only 2.75 litres and when there is exertion or exercise the beat will be in the region of 140 to 150 beats a minute.

To arrest this steady decline exercise is invaluable, swimming in particular. However for anyone out of condition whose idea of sport has until now been confined to watching it on television, you must take care before embarking on a strenuous fitness regime. Start gently, do not over-tax the body initially. If during or after a workout you feel dizzy see a doctor for a check-up. It is also advisable to stop smoking. A smoker is twice as likely to suffer a heart attack in his forties as a non-smoker.

A high level of cholesterol in the blood clogs the arteries so it is sensible always to keep to a minimum the amount of foods you know contain cholesterol. As we age, the walls of important arteries thicken thus making the passage of blood difficult. With the addition of cholesterol further clogging the passage, the heart has to work harder still and can be severely taxed as it tries to force blood through to where it is needed. It is this extra effort and strain that leads to strokes and heart attacks.

A certain amount of cholesterol is permanently present in our blood, the exact amount only calculable by blood analysis. At twenty the average content is about 180 milligrams rising to around 200 milligrams at thirty, 220 milligrams at forty and, at fifty the figure is likely to have increased to around 230 milligrams. Relative blood pressures for the same ages are around 122/76, 125/76, 129/81 and 134/83.

To keep your cholesterol levels down to an acceptable level avoid all animal fats and cut down on milk products and eggs. This means eating less meat fat, less fatty meats (like pork, mutton, duck and all sausage) and limiting yourself to small amounts only of milk, cheese and eggs (never more than three a week). The rule is always to avoid fried foods and use polyunsaturated spreads like margarine instead of butter. Salad oils though fattening in excessive quantity, being of vegetable origin, are polyunsaturated too and it is generally believed that they actually combat cholesterol by working to reduce its level in the blood. Olive oil is monosaturated which means it is neither saturated (fatty), nor polyunsaturated – but acceptable. All vegetables and fruit are free of cholesterol content.

Sex

At around forty sex drive is in no way diminished although for many the demands may sometimes change subtly. Sex, although enjoyable and vitally important, starts to become less compulsive and an additional pleasure of life rather than a necessity like food and drink.

With true aging – and by that we mean from sixty onwards – the testicles sit low in their scrotum which hangs lengthily instead of snugly close to the body and it can take a considerable time to reach erection. By seventy the situation declines further and desire begins to tail off but, by then, most men will have taken up other night-time interests like sleep or reading a good book so they worry little about the change.

The ability to have a continuing sexlife depends mostly on keeping in practice. And a fit body is more likely to have the right vitality and energy to respond to sexual stimulus than an unfit one. It is not unknown for men in their eighties to enjoy a (comparatively) active sexlife and have themselves a ball.

In the United States doctors interested in such matters have concluded that the angle of erection changes with age. At thirty, they say, the average erect penis thrusts about twenty degrees above the horizontal, at forty it is only just above the horizontal line at ten degrees and at fifty, just a dip below. Whatever the angle, it neither interferes with achievement or pleasure, nor does it impair the ability to achieve orgasm.

Now: The Good News

After the bad news, what can be said to have improved over the years for a man now between thirty-nine and forty-five?

Not much.

Usually he is wiser, more compassionate, more understanding, more secure. Generally he becomes more concerned with relationships than with achievement – the obvious exception being the freelance man whose future depends on being able to accumulate capital in order to cushion his retirement. Instead of feeling propelled to compete at work or within the social circle, men after forty enjoy better relationships with their families and wish to be with sons and daughters more for leisure. They begin to enjoy friends and neighbours more. People begin to matter.

As he glances into a mirror a fortyish man may not think he looks so good but to many people he is now at his most attractive with an indefinable element of sophisticated maturity. Unless something has gone dramatically wrong or his equilibrium is irrevocably shaken by the male-menopause, he will as yet only be just slightly off-peak in condition and whatever signs of decline he may spot they will be nothing he cannot handle.

For the record, true signs of aging are visible from about the fiftieth birthday onwards. To slow their approach: exercise for a firmer body, stronger heart, better circulation and healthy lungs; diet by eating sensibly and cutting out fats; give up tobacco (a cigarette smoker is likely to live ten years less than a non-smoker); drink only moderate amounts of alcohol (more than five drinks a day is not considered moderate but heavy). And if you are a sun-worshipper, use suncreams. The sun's ultraviolet rays dry out and stiffen the skin often making it blotchy with age spots. Leading cosmeticians claim that unless he is a nudist the best skin on a man of sixty is on his buttocks where the sun never sets.

f. On being young . . . or not

> *'The worst thing about facing up to age is going into shops and seeing things like leather jackets and jeans by designers like Armani, Versace and Venturi and knowing now that I can afford them I am too old to wear them. True fashion is for guys in their twenties.'*
>
> Michael, forty-five.

Until the male-menopause strikes few men are accurately aware of their age or aware of the true process of getting old. Or how they look. They see aging in others perhaps but not in themselves. In their eyes although they spot the occasional greying hairs and the morning-after baggy eyes, they see themselves as still around thirty and never remotely consider themselves like the middle-aged people they see in stores, hailing taxis or sitting placidly in airport lounges. Never.

So the moment a person refers to their correct age as being old or compares ages in the office or, at a party, attractive company in its twenties talks about forty as being *old*, it comes as something of a shock.

It is not a fear of being one step nearer the grave that worries them, they are upset because they have grown old without knowing it and without being prepared for it. Without so much as a single warning shot they now find they are on the wrong side of youth. Hello middle age; hello anxiety. Each man wakes to the conclusion that if he is going to make changes he is going to have to move damn fast. Or is it already too late?

This, say psychiatrists, is the root of the problems of the male-menopause: coming to terms with getting old, the fear of being old before one's time.

Curiously, without making a conscious decision a number of menopausal men face up to this by deciding to fight either by Living-Young – which means keeping up socially with the young set – or, by Dressing-Young – which means faking it by wearing clothes normally seen on men in their late twenties. Having one of these traits does not necessarily mean the menopausal man will also have the other.

Living-Young is the term used for men who have the desperate urge to *live* like the young of today. To adopt their mores and habits, their freer lifestyles, lovelife, values and attitudes to responsibility. They want only to spend their money on playing, on discos, dope and sex. To have fun. They see living-young as being-young. They will do anything rather than sit at home. Old people sit at home.

Dressing-Young affects a smaller group of men but we see them about nonetheless, usually in the company of attractive and undeniably young company.

These are the men whose clothes look either as if they were bought in the Seventies when the man considered he was at his dashing fashionable best (figure-hugging slim-fit shirts opened to the navel to reveal hefty gold chains and ornaments; denim jackets, leather belts with name-designer symbols on the buckles; designer sunglasses) or as if he bought them only yesterday with his credit card from a store that caters for the young set. This latter group will buy anything labelled 'new' or featured on the colour pages of magazines irrespective of the fact that the clothes are designed for much younger men whose bodies have youth, shape and mobility on their side. It is unfortunate for them that young clothes do not a young man make, but a figure of fun.

Both groups will spend heavily on aftershaves and colognes and liberally bathe themselves in the best of Aramis, Eau Sauvage, Givenchy, Halston, Polo, Saint Laurent and all the great names.

PART III

Sex: Go-Go or No-Go

Introduction

'The male-menopause does not exist. Men use it as an excuse when they can no longer get it up.'

Margaret, forty-three, divorcee.

Rumour would have it that if a man in his early forties takes a new lover or enjoys an affair or two (or more) you can blame it on the male-menopause. The marriage may be fine but the implication is what he wants is fun, adventure, excitement and, let's face it, more sex, sex with someone new.

To an extent this rumour is true. Most men given half a chance would jump at the opportunity of a dalliance and sex, male-menopause or not. It's history. It is balm for the man's ego and fun for his body.

In their early forties many married men find the urge initially kindled when they notice the attractions of a daughter's best friend or a son's girlfriend and deliberately set out to stimulate their own lives with a companion who is young and lively. In time an affair may start in the office or through a casual encounter in a restaurant, pub or at a party. The new young girl finds the man attentive, sophisticated and attractive; he finds her charming, young and irresistible.

In complete contrast to this ever-ready man however, the male-menopause can just as easily make a man withdraw totally from sex, especially if he already has a low libido. He will have a lack of drive, sexual urge and erection caused by reaction to the build-up of the emotional disturbances brought on by M-M. He loses all interest in sex but is, and this is important, psychologically disinterested and *not* incapable physically. After the crisis sexlife should resume.

Unlike a woman's menopause which is essentially due to physical change, the man's menopause is due entirely to the emotional crisis that upsets him at this turning point, the middle years of his life. As there is no noticeable hormonal change he becomes sexually neither infertile nor incapable, nor do his testicles shrink – no matter what old wives' tales might suggest. Whatever the rigours of his crisis he remains as virile as ever he was and should he switch off interest in sex, the switching off is temporary.

As for hormonal change, yes, there is a decline in the production of testosterone (the male hormone) but the decline is so slight and insignificant (and caused by the aging process not M-M) that it makes not one jot of difference to erection, performance, reproduction and enjoyment. Any sexual problems at this time are related entirely to outside matters like stress, not genitalia.

One obvious source for the rumours about hormones and a man's need to have booster injections of testosterone is attributed to the practice of those doctors and clinics who until recently made a habit of prescribing injections or hormone tablets as an easy way of treating the male-menopause in the apparent belief that if you give a man something to improve the performance of his penis, whether it works or not, he will believe in its efficacy and so will be miraculously cured of all his ills. A short course of hormone therapy *can* revive energy, health and libido in men after sixty but rarely is it any use to men around forty whose own production remains unimpaired and far from deficient.

In puberty testosterone is the masculinizing hormone that amongst its other actions makes the penis grow and pubic hair appear. By sixteen a man is at the peak of his fertility, a peak that lasts until he is about twenty when the production of testosterone slackens and slows down. This decline, however, is barely noticeable and years later around forty the fertility count remains high unless there has been an acute physical problem or illness. With the passage of time the production of testosterone continues slowing but the reduction is nonetheless hardly noticeable before a man reaches sixty. Some men go well into their seventies full of vigour and virility and start new families. Pablo Picasso and Charlie Chaplin are two fine examples.

Many, heterosexual or homosexual, can never have enough sex whatever their age. They are insatiable and enjoy variety. It flatters the ego, feeds their innate sense of masculinity and makes them feel good. Around forty this lust is hardly diminished. A man may take a little bit longer to come to orgasm than he did at twenty and perhaps his ejaculation is a little less powerful but his desire remains as strong as ever. In fact taking a little longer time during sex may make him a better lover: his orgasm is likely to be more intense and his partner will probably appreciate the longer lasting erection.

By forty a man will also have developed his own specific tastes as a prelude and as stimulation for sexual pleasure. Some enjoy a romantic candle-lit dinner to set the scene, others prefer to snatch their pleasures illicitly in the heat of a summer's afternoon after a good lunch. Many indulge in fantasy, playing out roles or dressing up and using toys, bondage and other devices. For others part of the pleasure is paying for it, buying sex and a few can only enjoy frenzied sex treating their partner roughly as they take their pleasure fast, selfishly, like a man possessed. To each his own. As a London therapist says:

'As long as it is pleasure and no one gets hurt anything goes and is good for you.'

Not every man suffers the anguish of sexual problems during the male-menopause but for the majority it seems as their egos falter and the emotional problems brought on by the crisis start making them question needs and values, so this becomes crunch time.

In one sore moment self-esteem can take a blow, the libido weaken, drive evaporate. Even a man with a normally high libido can be thrown off-course and sexlife, already finely tuned by emotional stability, takes an upward or downward turn. For the better or for the worse. A man can feel either ready for more loving and ripe for an affair outside his marriage or, ego shattered, he may turn away completely from sex, his sexlife grinding to a halt. It is go or no-go. The male-menopause has a lot to answer for.

Liberated homosexuals established in a promiscuous sexlife seem to have fewer worries at this time about sex drive possibly because in their freewheeling world there are many different roles that can be played with impunity. Subconsciously, like heterosexual men, they may begin to seek out younger and more exciting partners to prove their own attractiveness and to prove their power and appeal has not worn off with age.

a. All-systems-go

'All I want is to screw, screw, screw, drink and screw some more.'

Mid-menopausal exhultation.

To quote Dr Alex Comfort in *The Joy of Sex: 'The conventional male fantasy of being able to perform anytime, anywhere is wholly neurotic and impractical. Only the totally insensitive are all-time fucking machines like a stud-bull – and even stud-bulls have their off-days.'* But for many menopausal men this stallion fantasy builds up into mammoth proportions as they rush around trying to prove themselves virile. It is a balm to their ego and keeps their libido riding high.

Their lust is strong. They want sexual relationships with firm young bodies, with women of liberated lifestyles and women it does the ego good to be seen with in bistros, bars and hotels. And if the reason for this urge does not seem obvious, therapists who have given the subject much thought conclude that during the male-menopause being with someone attractive makes you behave differently and this, they say, is the whole point: you enjoy the different way you are behaving. Sexy young women make a man act and feel good.

> *'I could only think to myself: why should I still feel like sex with my wife? After eighteen years?'*
>
> Survivor, forty-six (new wife, twenty-five).

Once the seven-year-itch was cited as the reason a husband looked for sex elsewhere but now it is generally recognized that the itch is constantly around. In truth, everyone is likely to enjoy extra-marital sex given the right opportunity and certain knowledge that their infidelity is likely to remain secret and a man in an all-systems-go frame of mind during M-M considers the subject vital for life – especially if his marriage is stale and he thinks himself lonely or starved of affection. Tame home sexlife can encourage a man to seek out his pleasures elsewhere; he will fantasize how much better sex would be with someone other than his wife.

With a libido ticking over like a highly tuned motorbike many set out voyaging sexually, ready to seek out any sexual encounter. Not for them the routine pleasures of home sexlife but students, nurses, office secretaries and should the occasion arise, the wife's best friend. In fact almost every menopausal man in a Go frame of mind yearns for pleasure elsewhere ready to take risks and sacrifice the solid platform of his marriage for a brief, but hopefully secret, fling. The urge is great, driving and continuous. He *knows* just how much better sex is away from the marriage bed with someone young, full of ripe energy and longing for experiment. If he could he would give half his worldly goods for two weeks of paradise with a sexy young beauty at a beach resort; more for a lifetime with a fascinating fun beauty. If he can't get any of this together then he will make do with callgirls, prostitutes and massage parlours.

On what might be termed a more pedestrian level it is also true that many men are well-contented with their wives and families and seek an affair (or many) purely and exclusively for the pleasures such an affair will bring. These men have no intention of changing their home lives or replacing one steady and loving relationship with another. Like archetypal Latin Lovers, for these men an affair remains strictly an affair.

It is also true that not every man has the courage to conduct an affair or, indeed, would want to. Many when faced with an open opportunity will back away in panic, terrified of its implications, of what it might do to their marriage if anyone were to find out or how it would adversely affect chances for promotion.

In their lust for sexual adventure many will take to looking for new routes to sexual gratification instead of searching for pleasure with a nubile beauty.

For example. Some slip into the twilight world of voyeurism taking their pleasures vicariously and inhabit sex cinemas and clubs, happy to watch others at play, and, some turn to being peeping-toms prying on changing-rooms and neighbourhood windows. Seeking release through masturbation they may content themselves with video booths or purchase girlie magazines which they then keep hidden at home. A few take to exhibitionism and join the younger or older flashers in the park waving their genitalia at women or jumping out from behind trees, naked, giving frights to lady joggers and young mothers walking little children. In a lesser exhibitionistic streak some men 'show their bunch' (to quote an expression used by King's Road, Chelsea, boutique staff) and force their genitalia into prominent bunches down one trouser leg. This is usually a trait of aging homosexuals and heterosexuals over fifty but younger M-M men sometimes do it too.

Of course not all these diversions are symptoms exclusive to the male-menopause nor are they likely to affect all men equally as they pass through the crisis. Some behaviour patterns like flashing in the park are often symptoms of a mental disturbance that is totally unconnected with M-M and require psychiatric therapy.

In their search for experiment and experience many men turn to homosexual encounters 'just this once' and, having made an opportunity occur, will pretend their unusual actions are due entirely to over consumption of alcohol and claim not to remember a thing about the encounter the next morning. However, as a result to this just-once occurrence many find in themselves a latent homosexuality that they enjoy. With trepidation they then develop a habit of frequenting gay meeting places and a taste for serious homosexual friendships.

The homosexual relationships can turn out to be what they have always subconsciously sought and if their homosexuality is more than a passing phase for experiment or in answer to an occasional urge for bi-sexuality, then it can lead to the establishing of a secret life: a heterosexual life with a public face and a homosexual life in the shadows. The results can further complicate their already complex and shaky emotional state or, because their inherent homosexuality is no longer latent, they may take all known risks to lay foundations for a changed pattern of life. Many men come out of the gay closet because of M-M.

> *'When I found he was sleeping with a guy of twenty-four I was more relieved than shocked. At least it was a man. I could handle that. Had he been sleeping with a woman I would have doubted my own sexuality.'*
>
> Cristina, forty-two, divorcee, New York.

Obviously discovering homosexual love can take life to a dramatic point for a married man especially if, as is not uncommon, he then finds sex with a woman abhorrent and he can no longer make love to his wife. And should she discover the reason for his change, the moment of discovery can be hurtful. Only very few wives find themselves in a position to talk rationally to their husbands about the problem and only in a sophisticated circle can a wife discuss such matters with friends or family. As with heterosexual lapses in a good marriage she may conclude there is a lot to be lost and forgive him his lapse and it will take the man time to re-establish the marriage on a warm footing. With luck and no more (known) adventures the marriage enters a more mature stage.

And while some heterosexual men develop a taste for gay life it is not unknown at this juncture for gay men to take stock of their transient world and want to establish a heterosexual pattern. However unlike the heterosexual discovering latent emotions within himself, a gay man usually finds within himself a new maturity and a yearning to have a lifestyle most people would accept as normal and to have a secure family environment, preferably with his own children.

This does not mean these men necessarily foresake their gay lives although many can, and do. Most make marriages with wives who know of their gay pasts and assume that if the gay predilection is not over, at least it will not interfere with the calm of their lives, ever. Both husband and wife are seeking companionship and security with a mature marriage.

b. The No-Go Complex

> *'How can you think about sex when nothing about you is right!'*
>
> Mid-menopausal lament.

No erections, no orgasm, no interest, no fun.

While some dash about rampant, sex on the brain, an erection ready at a moment's notice, an equal number enter a No-Go limbo where the male-menopause brings their sexlife to a halt, the penis flaccid. It is the start of sexual trauma. Without appreciating what is happening to them they discover their sex drive has been curbed and they go into deep decline, each man terrified that his penis no longer works.

Why?

For no other reason than the fact that the unwanted mixture of depression, anxiety and fatigue that makes up the M-M crisis has created in them a despair far outweighing anything ever before experienced and debilitated both mind and body. Sexlife stops. The one activity that is recognized as being most conducive to relaxation and the perfect antidote to depression is the one activity their mind rejects. When the world appears to be on the verge of collapse, with his emotions in turmoil how can a man think of sex? Many cannot.

Tied in with this sense of being life's failure there may also be a fear of being a sexual failure. This could stem from an earlier failure and the fear of it being repeated or from the anticipation of criticism from a malicious or hostile partner. (Many Go-Go men also live constantly with the fear of failing to perform well as they rush into each encounter hoping to prove their continuing virility).

Change of sexual desire too can at this time lead to a total lack of urge. Though it might not seem like it to a man whose changing attitude to life has started his questioning his sexual tastes, the fact that he cannot have the sexual style he wants may lead him to abstinence or reliance on masturbation. He may want a new young lover, for example, or to dabble in a gay relationship and feel frightened of making advances in that direction for fear of rejection or making a fool of himself. He would rather be abstinent than foolish.

Redundancy from work is also a shattering blow for a man around his forties, the experience of losing his job hard to bear. At this age he sees the loss as a personal accusation or criticism of his work ability and knows there are few opportunities open to him for re-employment. With a death knell ringing over his work potential, sexlife hardly matters.

If a man is what is termed by many therapists as 'sex-lazy' his sexlife can tail off permanently.

Many men whose libidos are low are often considered sex-lazy too. They see sex as a burden they can well do without. For them sex is the occasional and rare performance they feel they have to give as a token of the physical proof they know their partners expect of them or, if they come from a religious background, simply as an activity to be enjoyed exclusively as a means to further procreation. Perhaps through either ignorance or lack of adventure for these men sex is not quite what they thought it would be so never do they feel a particular urge rising in them anyway. Perhaps their partners are sex-lazy too and delighted in their man's disinterest. In no time our sex-lazy man can retire from sex altogether, a retirement he looks forward to. The less he practises, the less likely he is to become sexually stimulated or active ever again.

Apart from the obvious emotional factors that wreak havoc on the sexlife there are also a number of additional factors peculiar to the male-menopause that can further compound the situation.

Menopausal-coincidence, for instance.

This is by no means a rare occurrence. Just as the husband meets his mid-life crisis face on, his wife embarks on her own climacteric with her own doubts and depressions and all the attendant doubts about encroaching middle age. Just as he is in need of reassurance so is she. She too is under emotional stress. Life together is problematic, misunderstandings occur and quarrels are inevitable. Unaware of each other's particular problems both partners can generate hostile emotions and bear grudges because of the lack of interest, sympathy and sensitivity being accorded them. He lays all the blame for his sex problems on her. If he is already sex-lazy he will opt out of sex permanently; sex-thirsty, and he will rush out seeking extra-marital fun.

Beginning to *feel* old may account for sexual depression in some men. It can make a man feel less sexually potent and, by beginning to feel not quite what he was physically a few years ago when he was younger, it increases the fear that he is in a sexual decline. Virility is under threat. Then, as if this is not bad enough, fear of physical failure in performance turns him yet further away from the thoughts of sex. It is only when he meets up with a (new) partner who stimulates him sexually and shows him the outward signs of enjoying a physical relationship with him that his fear passes.

For some men the worry about heart failure brings their sexlife to a halt.

These are the men for whom M-M develops the suspicion that there is something wrong with their hearts. Few check with their doctors but rather than take any risks they remember the old wives tales that with a heart condition you should avoid sex – and so they do. In his research in Britain, Dr Richard Bayou discovered that after one of the partners had suffered a heart attack, one-quarter of the couples enjoyed less frequent sex and another quarter opted out of sex altogether. The misapprehension is that if there is a heart condition sexual activity must stop, that good sex is too much for a weak heart to take. None have given up sex on doctor's orders.

The moment a man begins to doubt himself during the male-menopause whether it is in terms of career, family, money or security, his ego-balloon punctures and starts slowly to deflate. Self-esteem is damaged. The fear of performing badly the ultimate blow. Being constructive some turn to sexual counsellors for therapy for help while others, from continuing fear, turn to the simplicity of abstinence.

But as a London therapist says talking about abstinence and temporary celibacy: *'If god had meant man to be celibate he would not have invented the orgasm.'* See: *Surviving the Sex Crisis* (page 72).

PART IV

How To Survive

'A fool at forty is a fool indeed'

Fortune Cookie motto.

Introduction

> *'Take the male-menopause seriously. Make the adjustments you need and make the most of your life. Do not jeopardize your future.'*
>
> Therapist, London.

Overcoming the crisis successfully and emerging the other side to a better life can demand both a change in attitude and an adjustment to expectations on what you want from life. Neither compromise is easy to accept as both sound uncomfortably like admitting to failure or like giving up on current ambitions and ideals, the kind of capitulation that on the face of things seems cowardly and unmasculine.

But this is not so. Successful change demands careful planning not reckless action. And some bravery. Why not improve life while you can? Why not sort out new priorities, fresh ambitions, fresh ideals and fresh aims? And develop a new and successful lifestyle that offers scope for personal achievement and, more important, satisfaction.

Some of us may be changed by M-M and lead a life afterwards that is only distantly connected with life earlier. This is particularly true where marriage and work problems have been involved. Sexual tastes may change too and for some having tasted the joys of an affair, the taste becomes an addiction.

If you are susceptible there is nothing you can do about avoiding the symptoms of the male-menopause. Those that are going to affect you, will. But you can recognize them for what they are, that is, simply, symptoms, and bad though the reaction may be at least you know you are in good company with countless others and not on the verge of collapse or madness and that physically you do not have a terminal illness. If your sexlife does not improve overnight at least you know normal service will soon be resumed.

Jungian analysts subscribe to the old adage that life is one long day with the age of forty as its midday, a high-noon peak before the long afternoon and dusk with its setting sun. (Both Jung and Freud suffered mid-life crises.) And during the M-M years the past looks far richer than the future. But although the past may have been great why shouldn't the future be as good – if different? Survival lies in the ability to spot what is going wrong and make the correct decisions recognizing the changes you need in yourself and your lifestyle and adapting to them so that the future works to your advantage.

The male-menopause is a prelude to middle age and during this time of transition and upheaval we should take stock and appreciate the finer points of life and face the future with a plan for success rather than with no plan at all or with a spirit of gloom. If in a few years time you are going to be middle-aged why not lay the foundations at forty-plus for aging with style? Why look *old* when over the years you can improve like a good bottle of chateau burgundy. Maybe we cannot all look like Paul Newman or Clint Eastwood after fifty, or Cary Grant after sixty, but every man in his early forties can plan nonetheless to go into his middle years getting the most out of life.

Having identified the symptoms and embarked on survival remember the next real problem is going to be one of aging and knowing that there is no such thing as eternal youth. Nor is it possible to extend one's own lifespan radically. We are stuck with a body that is programmed to age but we can slow down its decay and make the most of it while there is life left in it.

How?

The Survival Course encompasses all basic recommendations. From mental attitude (ambition, family, sex), to diet (cut out fats), tobacco (quit smoking), alcohol (in moderation), and exercise (firmer muscles, healthier heart, stronger lungs in about forty-five minutes a week). Read on.

The Survival Course: The Emotional Route

'Demand less from life – and enjoy it more.'

Survivor, forty-five, London.

The male-menopause invariably strikes when life is at its best. Man is at about his peak, his career going along nicely, perhaps with a touch of fame, money problems are slight, the home comfortable and sexlife, inside or outside his marriage, good. There is nothing much at this point he cannot handle yet for no obvious reason the crisis starts.

The first step to survival is acceptance. Accept that the male-menopause exists. That you have it.

Accept it secretly if you wish and deny it publicly. Tell everyone the male-menopause does not exist. Most men do.

Acceptance helps clarify the difference between symptoms, cause and reaction. You know what is happening and why and even though this may not provide instant solution it does help you identify the reasons for the confusion. From the moment we stop being sceptical and accept what M-M is, we understand what is happening no matter how irrational it is and although the problems may remain the same as before, now we know what is causing them. Survival becomes easier.

Be Realistic

If before the male-menopause you were coasting along comfortably with life looking good and now, at this moment, the future looks bleak, by all means mourn the passing of the good old days – but look towards the future. Do not cling to the past and think only of past glories, nothing you can do will put the clock back. Move forward, capitalize on the past, on what you have already achieved and enjoyed, and plan the changes you feel you need.

Of course making changes is not easy, most aims and dreams are out of reach. In order to start the conditions have to be right, money has to be readily at hand and innumerable family and home conditions have to be resolved simply.

Only you know what it is that can add the extra fillip to your life but be realistic in terms of what it is you want. Whatever the changes, whether they are major (like changing your profession), comparatively minor (like keeping up with the boys) or flippant (like having an affair with a neighbour's wife), make sure you know the risks involved and that:

a. the opportunity for success exists;
b. what you are aiming for really is within your grasp;
c. the change you want is reasonable and not based on either wishful thinking or flight of fantasy.

Remember too that you will not change overnight and that basically you will always remain the same person. To create a total new way of life, if that is what you want, is rarely possible.

If worklife is the problem or if you think your marriage is comfortable but stale, do not walk out on either without first considering where you are heading and how you will survive. Equally important, consider first the repercussions. These can be financial, destructive and not least of all, hurtful to people around you. Move slowly. Do not cause irreparable damage to other people's lives.

This is a time when commonsense must dictate what can or cannot be done and most men, it seems, find all it takes to make their lives more acceptable is a simple adjustment. Wild moves while full of drama and charged with theatrical gesture rarely lead anywhere and are more likely to prove destructive rather than constructive. You may hate yourself for working behind a desk in a city office, for instance, and dream of running a puppy farm in a cosy, flower-covered village but how practical in real terms is this kind of dream even if you love dogs? Feeling restless is not reason enough for packing your bags, abandoning your family and putting the dog in the back of the car. You have to do your homework first and be maturely responsible. Consider what you already have and evaluate what is favourable and what is not. Take stock. Many things must be right. Wife? Lover? Home? Money? Work? Career? Capitalize on what is right. Be circumspect.

In making your alternative plans know what it is that you can *add* to your life to make it acceptable. If you have an interest in foreign languages or travel, or in amateur theatre, start by taking lessons or joining a club. Make your spare time more lively and stimulating and through this interest meet new people, widen your circle of friends and at the same time develop your own personal ability and creativity.

Sort out your ambitions. If at twenty you wanted to be a famous author there is no valid reason why now, about forty, you should not still strive for the same goals. But at forty it may be far too late to cling to ambitions that rely on youth or long periods of study and training. At forty it is too late to become a brain surgeon, fighter pilot or famous footballer – but then few make it at twenty-five either.

Whatever you decide and ultimately it is you alone who makes the decision, consider that you may also have a number of people dependent on you – wife, family, children and colleagues – and that your decision may have a serious effect on them. Let them have some say in your future plans, listen to their thoughts and comments.

And expect them to be critical.

No matter how realistic you are in your judgement and conclusions, in nine out of ten instances you can bet others will view your life as excellent and see no reason for any change, however minor it is. Few will approve or understand your motives.

Ambition

'A man without ambition is a man dead.'

Anon

Where ambition is concerned during the male-menopause a man may be struck in one of two ways, the severity of either emotion dependent entirely on the make-up of his personality. In extreme, either he becomes ambitious beyond all reason or, the opposite, he turns inwards, deflated and apathetic, with not one jot of ambition, seeing himself a failure. Fortunately most men hover somewhere between the two, alternating neither exclusively one way nor the other; sometimes fired with hope, sometimes crushed and making do with their lot.

Having little ambition makes survival difficult. Without sense of purpose no one can improve or change the quality of his life. Almost every situation in life demands some form of decision based on ambition in order to fulfil our innate need for success through achievement. In making a go of life and a success out of the future whether the prize is work or social it is imperative to be driven by aspiration or expectation. Life without ambition can only be, at best, tolerable.

Being driven by too much ambition can also make life difficult especially if the aim of the ambition is hard to obtain. People around you can suffer.

Take work as an example. Aiming for a senior management position may be exactly where you would like to be and from where you think you could show the world precisely how able and qualified you are, but promotion is not something you can control or predict. The management's rules for selection may not be governed exclusively by choosing on ability. And changing jobs by moving to another company is no easier. At forty-plus work abilities are rarely questioned, only age. Aim too high and disappointment may be inevitable.

The clue to using ambition as a means for survival lies not in fighting to beat all odds or aiming only for the highest prize, but in capitalizing on what you have already achieved and then making a few sensible compromises so that your future goals are not too high to reach.

And although we are inclined usually only to see ambition in the context of work, aspiration and expectation also apply equally to money, love, fame, travel, acquisition and future success as much as to the frivolous matters of life like sex. Of course aim high in what you wish to achieve but not so high that even on a good day disappointment is certain. Have ambition because it is vital to your life; but adjust your sights so that if you fail the blow to your ego is one you can take, not one that stuns you. Then, make plans again.

Personal Revision

'Be Yourself'

Therapist, London.

On reaching his forties every man should revise his attitude to himself and his world whether he is affected by M-M or not. This is the recommendation given by a considerable number of therapists. Know yourself, they say. Know your faults (but don't be weighed down by them). Know your good points too.

It is now, at this crucial age, that it becomes imperative to sort out who you are in terms of how you see yourself and what you want from life. Only by doing this can you move ahead successfully.

In this context revising your attitude to yourself does not mean being exclusively critical or sitting back with gloom as you compare yourself with the earlier man aged twenty-five and concluding that not only are you fatter and older but you are also tied with considerable responsibilities like mortgage, family and aging parents. Nor does it mean looking for the signs of becoming middle-aged. So you have put on an extra roll of flesh around the middle, fine. And added more wrinkles, yes. Most men have at this age. But now be honest with yourself. What should you expect from the next phase of your life? Is there any valid reason why that well-worn adage *life begins at forty* should not apply to you too?

Of course it goes without saying that in your self-analysis you should avoid using alcohol or drugs as an aid, thinking that only through their help can the real you come to the surface liberated and stimulated. It does not. Alcohol and drugs may create a cosy sense of wellbeing and a rosily enhanced view of your life but as a New York therapist points out to his patients, neither illusion is likely to be accurate or be any longer lasting than the effects of the drink or drug.

Do not fall into the trap either of examining yourself through a jaundiced eye so that all you see is failure. Seeing yourself as a failure is one of the most common reactions to the male-menopause and it affects all areas of life; sex and health as much as work. So take a positive and, if possible, optimistic attitude and see through the gloom.

Advice therapists offer their patients at this time is: concentrate on yourself. This applies to all men during M-M and if it sounds like selfish consideration contrary to everything we have been taught since childhood, it is. It is only by concentrating on yourself that you can improve your life.

'Concentrate on yourself,' one therapist says. *'Sort out your life to your satisfaction. Apart from certain goals affecting careers, for most of us we have been trained in our lives to look outwards but now the new rule is: look inwards. Consider yourself first. Give yourself new priorities and aims. Get into new projects or travel or hobbies that will improve your life satisfaction. Do not accept that for you life has no meaning or has to be dull and boring. If it is, you only have yourself to blame.*

'If life begins at forty – and why shouldn't you begin again? – start out

by being yourself. Be honest. Look for personal affection and contentment. Let your humour come out. Try mocking yourself. Have fun.'

A conclusion to draw is that although middle-age may be around the corner and life is undoubtedly, if subtly, going to be different, the difference should be of your making and on your terms. By your choice and by making revisions about yourself and your expectations.

Be Positive

Change your mind when you have good reason, but when you take up an idea be positive, make your action at that moment with enthusiasm and commitment.

Nothing is more unsettling to life than indecision, whether it is your own or other people's. This applies as much to homelife as worklife. Since childhood we have all been trained to accept decisions and to live along lines designated by someone's ultimate conclusion and although often we may disagree with the final reasoning, for most of our lives we feel comfortable when decisions are made, we know where we stand. In simple instances it may be a case for deciding which movie to go to or where to eat. Or it might be less frivolous and demand serious consideration like which work offer to accept, which apartment to buy, when to get married, whether or not to divorce. In each instance a decision is made by being positive, a situation resolved by a decision taken.

Of course everyone is entitled to change their mind or opinion as they see fit and should do so. No decision should be seen as necessarily binding if good reasoning proves otherwise. But until for good reason you change your mind, stick by your decision.

And should you find you have reached an incorrect conclusion, worry not. Change again with a positive decision. Situations alter as fresh facts or influences become evident. When fresh facts present themselves each problem has to be reconsidered afresh.

In survival generally, it is vital to be positive in action and pursue decisions with commitment. Being indecisive during the male-menopause only adds to the worry of being a failure.

Change Emotionally

Although this may sound like a carte blanche solution to life for some of us, changing emotionally means expanding your interests, not discarding a wife or lover like an old shirt while you give chase to another – even if you are bored and have grown apart with personalities maturing and changing direction.

To change emotionally you must alter your life in such a way as to be able to move on to a richer plateau with fresh interests and commitments. Do not give up a life you are enjoying but accept that with time your tastes have changed slowly. You are beginning to ask and expect different things from life and for the future. Even if you could remember the priorities you had in your twenties or thirties they are not likely to be the same as those you have now. Involve yourself more in additional interests that will broaden your lifestyle and stimulate you either mentally or physically, or both.

Expand your interest and give yourself new goals. Find activities that relax you and add an emotional sense of contentment. This is not a sign that you are getting old, but of progression. To get the most from life you need the pleasure of indulging in some form of relaxation. It can come through sport, listening to opera or taking country walks with the dog. Emotionally expanding the mind can come through selective reading, studying a language ready for travel, joining a club.

At around this age it is easy to get into a rut and let your life slowly stagnate. Without firm action while the opportunities exist and without an emotional re-charge, the future could be dull or worse, boring.

Control Thinking

Should doubts, depression and feelings of failure or futility take hold, recognize them for what they are, symptoms of M-M, and try to create a way to overcome them by thinking or doing something different. The recommendation is: control your thoughts and block out depression by taking evasive action.

This may not be easy at 3 a.m. as you lie in bed, your problems crystal clear and engulfing you while everyone else is apparently blissfully asleep. There is nothing quite as effective at night as a parade of personal problems for instilling a sense of life-panic and misery.

But, as they say, think about an itch and you begin to itch. If in a cinema you think your ankles are being bitten by a flea, in no time you feel as if a flea is having a party in your pants. If on a boat you worry about being seasick, you are seasick.

Emotional problems, therapists say, arc no different. If you think about them, you worry about them; worry about them and they become magnified out of all proportion. Especially at night.

Of course where true problems exist it would be head in the sand, ostrich policy to ignore them and hope that by doing so they will evaporate. But invariably problems based on self-doubt, the very essence of the male-menopause, do exactly that. They resolve with time.

Trying to avoid thinking about problems is no easy matter. Some men find at home, whatever the time, an easy solution is switching on TV or taking the dog for a walk, or jogging for fifteen minutes. Many head for the kitchen to cook up a special dish. At work solutions vary from taking an extra coffee break to making a social telephone call.

By all accounts there are no shortcuts that will work for all men uniformly. Perhaps this is because problems vary man to man. Whatever works for you, only you can discover. But the aim is simple: to take your mind off internal panic and to be able to return to facing reality as it is, real and uncoloured by the gloom brought on by M-M.

Stop Complaining

'Many menopausal men cannot stop themselves complaining about every facet of their daily lives. Incessant complaining achieves nothing except heightened disquiet and a loss of friends. How can anyone be sympathetic with a man who whines?'

Psychoanalyst, London.

It is unfortunate that one of the reactions to M-M is an inability to see any situation or happening in other than a bad light and to take any set-back, however minor, as a personal affront or defeat. Nothing is quite what it should be or what you believe righteously it should be.

Without realizing what is happening many men complain privately and publicly at every turn and it is not until someone, a relative or friend, quite likely in ill-humour, points it out that they then notice how they are behaving. (Often they will believe their complaints are well justified nonetheless.)

Of course there is a lot in normal everyday life to complain about but it is difficult for anyone to be with a man who constantly grumbles and who appears impossible to please or permanently in a moaning mood. Around him tempers fray easily and people are inclined to shy away, short on sympathy. The sad fact is the more he complains the more likely he is to be disturbed by M-M and the more his emotional equilibrium is at risk.

If you are in a complaining phase and must complain, do so only about major issues or when complaint is fully justified. World affairs, politics or taxation seem acceptable areas and so possibly are occasions of faulty laundry service or restaurant food that is bad. But if you feel you must complain about your boss or about how badly your lover is treating you make sure you complain to someone with a sympathetic ear (who has not heard your complaints before) and permanently avoid complaining about how badly life is treating you.

As all therapists would advise, stop demanding sympathy. Get out and start trying to make the alterations you want to your life as it is your responsibility alone to sort out your life to your satisfaction. A man who complains incessantly is a bore, not sympathetic.

Work Reversal — or the Career Nosedive

> *'How can I face up to another twenty years in the same old job? Retirement or death can't be the only way out.'*
>
> Mid-menopausal lament.

There is no better way for a man to avoid the male-menopause totally than promotion or a new job that gives him extra prestige, power, influence and money. This cements his emotional foundations and gives substance to his life. If there were doubts until this moment about a stale marriage or the lust for sexual voyaging, work achievement and success invariably puts matters to right so that the next phase of his life is as controlled and as full of contentment as he could hope it to be.

For most men, although ambition has fired them to aim for higher goals, the success they have achieved in their career climb has come from a fortunate mixture of ability, work aptitude and acceptable personality. And luck. And being in the right place at the right time has probably boosted their chances of promotion too.

But at forty, just as choice and opportunity become less, so many men feel trapped by the work they once considered if not enjoyable, at least acceptable, or at worst, tolerable. Now they feel suffocated. What they want above all else is a new job to give them a personal sense of achievement and success.

But what can be done when worklife becomes intolerable and a daily drudge and when, after a number of years as the bright-eyed executive ripe for promotion, others younger or less qualified seem to be getting ahead, and what was once a career in ascendence now appears to be a career taking a nosedive? Or, when you feel trapped by your dependence on your work (for money responsibilities) and all you can see are the prison-wall limitations your work represents? In this situation every man feels resentful. He feels embittered and as he is under stress, he is prone to increased anxiety and, perhaps, a heart attack.

The regrettable fact of life is that around forty, whatever your field, opportunities are less rather than more. A man may have considerable expertise and talent to offer but at forty-plus he will find he is over-qualified for some jobs and too old for others where training or study is required.

If you are among the fortunate who can readily change jobs, the solution offers you no problem but for any man without firm prospect of a new job ahead the answer remains problematic. Dropping out or quitting without first finding new work is both foolish and risky and no one should move without taking full, mature reflection and consideration. Every man has responsibilities to himself and others.

To achieve some satisfaction and change you must first take stock of what you have. Value carefully. How good is the lifestyle it affords you? Is the work element of your day so intolerable that you cannot live with it? Do you hate the people you work with?

If the prospects of promotion seem dimmer now than they did five years ago, are you dissatisfied with what you have achieved? Is there another facet you could add to your life to make your life generally more tolerable or, better still, more enjoyable?

The truth is that while the male-menopause exerts its gloomy side effects, every work problem becomes magnified and seemingly insoluble; every dislike takes on mammoth proportions. Problems can seem insurmountable even when they are not. Prejudices and pet-hates start to become the focal point to life simply because they feed two of the male-menopause's basic symptoms: depression and self-doubt. Work reversal fuels these symptoms.

To survive: do nothing dramatic.

First try to adjust to what appears to be a reversal of all your hopes and ambitions by quietly accepting events because the reversal could sort itself out with time and then, if you remember the problems at all, you may wonder what all the disquiet was all about. Find extra activities that will make your leisure hours fun and fulfilling; make your leisure time an antidote to your work. Above all, move and make changes only slowly. Have no regrets.

Apply for new jobs too, but be realistic. There are going to be many men in the same predicament (in M-M and without) going for the job. If you have only an outsider's chance of being interviewed do not be surprised or offended if no one calls you.

And in looking for a job, are you helping yourself as much as you could? If the job you are going for is within reach, will your appearance help you get it? Have you let yourself go within the last few months? Is your appearance going to let you down? You have to dress successfully (see later chapter). At every interview good appearance scores.

While you consider changing career because you feel you are stuck in a rut consider whether the job you already have might be better with a branch office or in another city or country. Can you transfer? A change of environment may be all it takes to revive your interest and career.

And look back. Do you change your job every two years for no more reason than the feeling of discontentment? Many men have what is seen as a two-year lifespan in one job, no more. These are the rootless kind of men many companies make sure they do not employ. Hold on to your job longer so that on your c.v. it looks as if you change jobs with ambition or for a promotion to something better and not because you ran out of steam.

Surviving the Sex Crisis

> *'The earlier in life a man becomes sexually active and the more frequently he, for want of a better word, performs, the longer and later into his life his sexlife continues. The sexual system needs to be kept fully active if it is going to function properly.'*
>
> Sex therapist, London.

First rule: do not worry about sex. *Second rule:* loosen up.

And if there is a third rule for the man in a No-Go world it is: *keep practising.*

No man's life should come to a complete halt sexually because of the male-menopause but it does happen. And finding sexlife faltering, and fearing that impotence lies in wait just around the corner, makes this crisis reaction probably the most shattering of all within the catalogue of M-M symptoms. But, says one of London's leading sex therapists, by using mind over matter, the shortage or absence of drive should not be an impossible problem to solve. After all we know that there is no hormonal change taking place so that as soon as the male-menopause is survived, life returns to normal (or maybe to a new level that will become regarded as 'normal') and normal service should be resumed sexually. The causes are cerebral not physical. With some planning sexlife could return sooner (than later).

During M-M a lack of drive must be understood to be only temporary, a set-back but nothing more. The failure we know is in the mind and not the penis.

As therapists insist and so many studies and books express, even under perfect conditions a man is not a sex machine who can perform the moment a button is pressed, no matter how much he would like to be or what movies and pulp fiction tell us. Sexual responses are governed by emotions, fears, expectations and experience.

In their parlance sex therapists refer to this impotent phase as 'psychological impotence' defining, as we know, that the problems are caused exclusively by the emotions. (Impotence is not being able to achieve an erection or an orgasm and is not to be muddled with infertility which is a temporary inability to produce a child. Infertility is not a symptom of M-M.) No-Go is not a peculiarity exclusive to the male-menopause and countless numbers of men the world over are concerned with it every day. Two particular physical problems can be involved: premature ejaculation (which is when a man reaches orgasm too quickly, sometimes almost as soon as intercourse begins) and ejaculatory incompetence (which is having no difficulty getting an erection but failing to come to orgasm), both due entirely to anxiety. Like all solutions to M-M the answers to the problems are linked with learning new techniques and relaxation, solutions that sex therapists in consultation will explain fully or are found in well-known studies like Masters & Johnson's *Human Sexual Inadequacy.*

In short, the essence of the advice is that survival comes through the mind; loosening up on attitudes of what can be fun the most helpful pill of all. Sex should be fun; impotence never is.

For many men the simple solution of cutting down on alcohol helps, for although alcohol may make you feel good temporarily and give you inspiration, too much can numb the system and block out chances of erection. And taking regular exercise boosts vitality, the exercise contributing to making the body into a fit machine. Vitamin-E, often called the sex-vitamin, and Ginseng, the root said to have aphrodisiacal powers, have given some men the increased urge they seek, though the powers of both the vitamin and Ginseng to improve sexlife have been debunked by the medical profession. Vitamin-E is found in wheatgerm, dark green vegetables, wholewheat and eggs and can be bought in oil-based capsules. Short-term therapy is usually recommended as in the region of 200 to 400mg a day for about four weeks.

Nor should you forget masturbation, privately or with a partner. It does not, as therapists are quick to point out, make you go blind or grow hair on your palms – as schoolboy lore usually has it. Their word is that the more sexually active your body is, the more quickly you get back into the swing of things, the longer your sexlife lasts as you get older.

Consider too that it has been established the more sexually imaginative a couple are, the more frequently they will enjoy sex, the more pleasure both will derive and, in fact, during the menopause it is vital to reconsider your ideas on sexual demands and responses, on what you should or should not do, on who does what to whom and when. Consensus of opinion today promotes the theory that applies as much to the jaded as to the temporarily impotent: anything goes as long as no one is hurt. (This definition perhaps should be revised for sado-masochistic circles.)

By forty every man should be aware of the sexual variations and alternatives available to him and his partners. So the true meaning of loosening up may be: experiment. Be less inhibited about oral sex, masturbation and fantasy pleasures. Enjoy what you are doing or having done to you.

In many circles sexual voyaging, especially that of having an affair, is morally condemned but it has to be accepted nonetheless as a fact of life today that sexlife is freer than ever it was and that both men and women often enjoy secret sexlives outside their marriages.

But whereas a bachelor conducting an affair can be regarded as acceptable because there is always the off-chance that the affair is a prelude to permanence, that is, marriage, for a married man to do so he can only be seen in one light, bad. He is unfaithful, a sinner.

Given half a chance most men would jump to the opportunity of putting their sexual dreams into action. It's history. A dalliance of this sort is balm for the ego. However, if you are a man of affairs, although no one can control your actions, be careful not foolish. To you, your sexlife may be simply an irresponsible pleasure with no further commitment but a wife, family, lover or boss may not think of it in such light terms as you do. Many people will feel emotionally hurt, shocked and let down. Remember the consequences and what it is you stand to lose. On discovery, with some justification, you may squarely blame the male-menopause for your lust, but will anyone else?

That said, even after the male-menopause has faded, do not forget that just as in the good old pre-menopause days, sex is not always as regular a part of daily life as a cup of coffee, scrubbing teeth or watching TV. If there is an absence do not take it too seriously. As one survivor whose marriage met with the No-Go crisis and flourishes now with a new batch of children says with some humour:

'We have sex almost seven days a week now. Almost Monday, almost Tuesday, almost Wednesday . . .'

On Dressing-Young

When a man's face and body no longer match those of the gang, wearing boutique clothes designed for men fifteen years younger creates an appearance that verges on the ridiculous. And selecting a hairstyle because it looks good on a trainee at the office or on young television stars only compounds the impression.

So does the wearing of youth-cult trimmings like mirrored spectacles, bushy moustaches and heavy trucking shoes, and swinging along with a gym bag slung across the shoulder emblazoned with the latest sports name logo is best left to the gay set.

Wearing the status symbols of your own youth does not help either. Gold chains around the neck hung with clusters of gold charms, for example, the shirt open to the navel to reveal all and moccasins with an initialled gold bar, they all date back to the Seventies. So do leather belts with designer buckles. Clinging to the trappings of the past is fine for a time but as you get older – and you will – so these trappings put you into a category that dates you. You look peculiar not fashionable.

It is better by far in both social and career life to develop a style that makes you look yourself, to stand out stylishly so that your clothes project a personal image that is at once individual and successful. You do not have to spend a fortune changing your wardrobe or take to conforming to the standard ideas of elegance by wearing navy blue suits or blazer and flannels. The styles you choose must project you the way you are comfortable.

See *Dressing Successfully* (page 96).

On Living-Young

It may be fun for a while, but for how long? Ask yourself: are you being ridiculous trying to groove all the time? Is it always you who picks up the tab? If you are married does your wife want to keep up with you or is your marriage at risk? And, for how long do you think you can keep up this highlife without collapse?

It goes without saying that on reaching his forties man is no longer the same specimen he was in his twenties. He may think of himself as being the same and looking the same, but in reality? Rarely. Few are.

Aping youth with its freewheeling lifestyle and late nights can be fun and if you are in the grip of M-M it is probably preferable to be out on the town, up-high and partying, rather than at home sitting with a magazine and depression. But you must recognize that if you are out with a young gang (and, most likely, keeping up with the help of drink or drugs) you are only passing for young and that others see you for what you are, a man entering his forties, on the verge of middle age. Even if you have made yourself into the fun person at the party. Only similar men struggling with M-M partying alongside you are fooled by your energy. Or men far older.

Face up to it. You are no longer young — but you are not old either. You are somewhere in between. Have fun certainly but do it sensibly and at no risk to your health, family or future. Don't be the fool at the party who pays the bills and takes the gang back to his place for a nightcap and some music. Be the man people want to invite to their parties, the one they look forward to seeing but the one who goes home at a reasonable hour, his image intact, with his friendships close and valuable rather than transient.

The same reservations apply to dressing-young. Let people like you for what you are not the fake image you are projecting. Life is not passing you by; you are just not the man you were many years ago.

A London therapist says: *a man who projects a false image of himself, through clothes or the way he lives, fools himself. In the long run living-young and dressing-young, whether he does either consciously or subconsciously, only contribute to making life less easy in the future. If he is not careful he will find the fact that he is getting older over the next few years the most depressing years of his life. The gap between forty and middle-age is not much. The sooner he adjusts to the changes the better and, quite likely, the more successful he will be. The forties really can be the best years.*

Forward

By general consensus the advice is: look forward. Not back.

This may sound trite and obvious but as the old adage so succinctly sums it up, life is what you make it and the future at this point is all that matters.

The recommendation is to take your time, advice that could as easily be given to men in their twenties and thirties. Work towards creating an environment that pleases and take your pleasures slowly. No man should feel cheated by life. The male-menopause may create an unsettling period but only the weak could live through it without new plans, new tastes and new ambitions.

And having looked to the mind, don't forget the body. Forty is not old – for anything. Get your physical image right and use it to express the way you want to be. Go all out for success. Read on.

The Survival Course: The Physical Foundation

> *'After forty a man can look his best only if he respects his body. An unfit man looks what he is . . . an unfit man. That's hopeless!'*
>
> Health Club instructor, London.

Although the problems of the male-menopause are essentially emotional this does not mean the externals or the wellbeing of the body should be ignored in the pursuit of survival and improvement of quality of life. Not only does a fit man survive the rigours better than an unfit one but a healthy and groomed man goes on to better things as he projects his own best image, one that is neither frayed at the edges nor worn out.

This does not mean you have to use expensive face creams, wear designer label colognes and go jogging for an hour each day. It is more a matter of commonsense, some careful grooming based on cleanliness, sensible eating patterns and a few exercises to keep the body in trim. And a health check-up.

It takes only the smallest amount of time and effort to achieve the best. As aging begins to take its inevitable toll why not age decently rather than decrepitly? There is nothing wrong about a man taking care of the way he looks – and there is everything to be gained by his doing so. Men who arrive in their forties looking good do so only because in the twenties and thirties they took care of how they looked. Men who look good in their fifties do so because in their forties they took extra care and no matter the pressures they were under never let themselves go to the dogs. Whatever his age it is never too late for a man to start caring for himself. All he needs are the guidelines and a little effort.

a. Health and Check-Ups

Make an appointment with a doctor for a total check-up.

At around forty this is a sign of wisdom and careful body-management not hypochondria, the sign of a man determined to survive life in the best possible healthy way.

At about this age serious ailments are inclined to strike men, the problem ills brought on primarily by the pressures of modern life, like stress, and those that have developed with our society as we have grown more affluent, like heart disease. Heart disease today is to men what breast cancer is to women. *One man in every ten now aged thirty-five will die from coronary heart disease before he reaches sixty.*

If more men had regular check-ups this figure could be lessened considerably. Problems could be identified sooner and medication or treatment could begin before they became grave or possibly fatal. It is a comforting fact despite this pessimistic outlook however that although many men do rush to their doctor in panic fearing the worst and thinking they have the symptoms of a chronic heart condition, an estimated fifty per cent of them will have not a heart problem but chest pains brought on by those two now over-familiar reactions to today's life: stress and anxiety.

Independent health screening centres to carry out check-ups are being established in a number of major cities by medical groups – in London one run by the British United Provident Association is known internationally – but if he wishes any doctor can instigate the most essential tests himself and so keep costs down. (Medical centres are expensive. Fortunate are those valued executives working for far-sighted companies who are sent to these centres as a matter of policy and insurance.) The comprehensive tests cover problems peculiar to men in this age group and are designed to show up hidden troubles should they exist. As a matter of survival as much as for peace of mind, every man after forty whether he is in the grip of M-M or not, should have himself checked.

After discussing the patient's medical history and lifestyle the first tests invariably concern the heart. A doctor listens to the beat, checks the pulse and takes a reading of the blood pressure. If there is anything unusual he may recommend a visit to a heart specialist for an electrocardiogram reading to check where the abnormality exists. At medical centres electrocardiogram readings are taken as a matter of course.

If there is a blood pressure problem tablets are prescribed to bring the reading to an acceptable level. Many men are recommended low-fat or low-salt diets.

The strength of the lungs is tested by the simple means of blowing a number of times into a small machine and blood and urine samples are taken to check the efficient functioning of the internal mechanisms like liver and kidneys and, amongst other checks, to spot any signs of diabetes or anaemia. In a screening centre they will also x-ray the chest and carry out a more detailed physical examination that includes tests for rectal cancer and the more basic checks for sight and hearing as both deteriorate as we get older. At a screening centre tests will take up to three hours to complete.

Everyone in the Western world knows the hazards of smoking tobacco but many still continue to do so. If you smoke, quit. Two out of every five men who smoke die before they are sixty-five and it has been calculated that a smoker aged thirty-five will live five years less than his equivalent who is a non-smoker. Cigar and pipe smokers are also at risk even though many would kid themselves they are not. Where cigarettes damage the lungs and cause cancer, cigars and pipes contribute to cancer of the mouth, pharynx and larynx. The risk a man takes smoking are out of all proportion to the pleasure the habit gives.

Alcohol in moderation is acceptable but during M-M a man can easily go overboard and become dependent on it for its relaxing effects, finding he can only go about life if he is supported by vodka and other spirits.

In Britain social drinking is generally considered as about five measures of spirits, wine or beer each day. In this context the official British measurement establishes that ½ pint of beer, 1 glass of wine, 1 glass of sherry and 1 tot of spirits each equals 1 unit of alcohol. More than five drinks a day and not only do you run the risk of alcohol dependence but also the risk of damaging your liver and probably incurring problems at home and at work. A man with a blotchy complexion, impeded speech, erratic action and poor memory is an example of a man who drinks.

For anyone trying to diet, alcohol can be a particular enemy. Not only is it high in unnecessary calories but it also undermines willpower. An alcoholic will lose his appetite but for most men the more they drink the more they can eat of carbohydrates and fatty foods.

To survive, go carefully with drink and try to have regular days when you drink little or nothing at all.

To prevent hangovers, the solution is simple. Drink no alcohol.

To make hangovers less likely, drink less alcohol and at the same time or a little later drink large quantities of water. Sparkling mineral water seems to help the system best and aid the liver in its recovery but colas and other non-alcoholic drinks should work equally well. (Obviously the preference here should be for sugar-free drinks.) A substantial but non-fatty meal will also buffer the alcohol's effect.

Should you get a fierce hangover the best action is to first drink a large glass of water to combat the body's dehydration and then have a good breakfast of fruit, juice and whatever else you normally enjoy for breakfast. Do not start the day with a strong cup of black coffee and a couple of favourite painkillers; as soon as their effect wears off so the hangover returns with a vengeance. Eat lots of toast and, having lined the stomach successfully, only then take your painkillers. Resolve to drink less in future.

And drugs? What can be said that is not already common knowledge. Every man knows the risks involved with drugs whether the drug is marijuana, barbiturate, tranquillizer, amphetamine or opiate like cocaine, heroin, opium or morphine. (Habitual users of heroin become impotent.)

In many circles drugs have become part of social conformity – a man takes the drug to show he is one of the gang – or, to show he has money just as much as for pleasure. Whatever his reason, the risks remain the same: considerable.

Because sexlife becomes a focal interest during M-M many menopausal men in an all-Go world find themselves indulging freer lifestyles and so highly at risk with what are sometimes termed the 'social' diseases which are venereal diseases, the positively anti-social diseases. These can only be caught through sexual contact because the bacteria or organisms live in a person's infected genitalia, mouth or anus where they have been put through earlier sexual activity. Tongues, fingers and lips as well as the penis will transport them person to person.

At first sign of any unusual genital symptoms a doctor must be consulted and treatment started. One health recommendation worth considering if you have an active and liberated sexlife outside a normally, exclusively private relationship is that you wash with soap and water before and after each encounter, and urinate. To guard against gonorrhea and non-specific urethritis wear a condom if possible. None of these precautions are foolproof but they are a wise precaution and will provide some protection. If you think someone is over-generous with his or her sexual favours, avoid them.

The following are symptoms of the main sexually transmitted diseases (excluding AIDS which is a subject unto itself). Many of the symptoms can be due to a cause unconnected with veneral disease but, whatever the cause, if you have any doubtful symptoms consult a doctor or clinic. This is especially important advice for many homosexuals who have a promiscuous lifestyle and experience anal intercourse.

Gonorrhea: This is an acute infection of the genito-urinary tract that is contracted only through sexual or anal intercourse. It is nonsense that it can be caught from a lavatory seat or an infected towel or sheet as the gonorrhea organisms die if they are not nurtured within a warm body.

Infection is usually obvious three to five days after intercourse. The first sign is soreness when passing water and later this turns to a burning sensation and a thick discharge begins to drip from the penis. Without prompt attention the infection can spread so that the bladder becomes painful and inflamed. Acute infection may spread to the testicles and in time cause sterility.

Treatment is by antibiotic injection, two usually, probably penicillin, accompanied by a short course of tablets to ensure the organism is effectively killed off. During treatment you must not drink alcohol or have intercourse. Genitals must be washed twice daily with soap and water and a towel must be put aside for the affected person to dry themselves, a towel that will be used by no one else.

Checks are usually made one week after diagnosis and a final check-up is usually made three months later for a clean bill of health.

Syphillis: A small ulcer usually develops on the man's penis or woman's vulva about three weeks after intercourse with an infected person. It is a highly infectious disease where organisms multiply at such a fast rate that within thirty minutes of being infected the organism has infected the bloodstream.

The first sign of syphillis is the small ulcer on the penis which may appear as a pimple or hard chancre. The ulcer could appear around the mouth or anus. Glands then begin to swell. If any of these symptoms develop within ten to ninety days of intercourse a man must visit a doctor to have the ulcer diagnosed.

Syphillis is easily curable and it is believed that if it were possible to treat everyone currently infected with the disease, within a period of one month the disease could be eradicated completely.

The cure is by a course of antibiotics like penicillin injected over a period of about fourteen days.

Unless a man is treated when the ulcer is present the disease can continue to develop and six to eight weeks later he may begin to suffer headaches, sore throat and skin rash. Some men develop grey, flat growths in the mouth and around the anus.

It is customary for a check-up to be carried out by means of blood tests for about twelve months to ensure the disease has been cured.

Genital Herpes: This is a virus condition similar to the facial cold sores that sometimes appear around the lips except that in this instance the sores are around the genital or anal areas. A few days after being infected the sores appear. They are painful, burning and often weeping. After four days they probably dry up and within ten days only a faint set of scars remains.

At this point the disease appears to have gone but, and this is important, it is only dormant. Although new remedies and medicines are being introduced constantly there is not yet a guaranteed cure. After an interval of weeks, maybe months, the herpes reappear. Cream and ointments will calm the sores.

Genital herpes is highly contagious and a man with herpes on his penis will undoubtedly affect his partner during sexual play. As a rule sex should be avoided until herpes has disappeared but the infected person may still be contagious. It has become the accepted norm in some circles for infected persons to mention that they are carriers of the virus even when their own cases are dormant and appear to have disappeared. This gives the prospective partner opportunity to change his or her mind if the risks involved are more than he or she is prepared to take.

Non-Specific Urethritis: Often known by the bare initials N.S.U. this is an infection termed non-specific because there appears to be no known specific cause for it unlike gonorrhea or syphillis. But it is sexually transmitted.

About ten to thirty days after intercourse, usually with a casual partner, a slight discharge appears from the penis. Passing water may be painful or accompanied by a burning sensation. The need to pass water probably becomes more frequent.

During early stages the symptoms are similar to gonorrhea so a doctor will carry out an examination and test the discharge.

Treatment is usually with antibiotics like tetracycline. During treatment both sexual intercourse and alcohol must be avoided.

Genital Warts: These are single warts or clusters that suddenly appear around genital or anal areas. They are highly contagious and spread during the active moments of sexual intercourse because of a virus that enters the skin. It remains dormant for up to three months. When it becomes active the warts form.

On the penis the warts can appear either on the foreskin or on the skin edge beneath the glans head of a circumcised penis. They itch.

Treatment is by ointment or cauterization.

Trichomoniasis: This is an infection of the vagina that causes discharge, itch and smell. A man not wearing a condom during sex may have his penis infected too.

Treatment is a short course of tablets.

In the strict medical sense only gonorrhea and syphilis are venereal diseases, the others are infections. And there are two more problem conditions that can be caught genitally, infestations. These are pubic lice and scabies, infestations by parasites or mites passed on by body contact.

Pubic lice, or *crabs* as they are commonly called, are the genital versions of the head lice that can infect adults and children alike. These parasites burrow into the skin around the pubic hair shafts. On the skin the lice appear as tiny grey-brown dots; their minute eggs as tiny white clusters clinging to the hair. Pharmacies sell ointments for treating the condition.

Scabies, *the itch,* are caused by a mite that burrows into the skin and causes fierce irritation and itch. The female mite lays her eggs beneath the skin where they hatch about five weeks after incubation. Treatment involves painting the itchy patches and most of the body with a chemical solution.

b. Grooming

It is not unmasculine for a man to want to look good and take care of the way he looks – his hair, his face or his body. There is nothing wrong, whatever his age, in wanting to look his best and using toiletry preparations to help achieve this. Exercise strengthens the body; grooming takes care of its externals.

But although many men survive on a routine that embraces a daily shave followed by a dash of aftershave (probably a relic of Christmas bounty) and a quick go with a deodorant, plus a twice-weekly shampoo, in the long run they would possibly do better if they made a little more effort and followed a sensible routine with sound guidelines. Most of us would.

At around forty – if you will excuse what sounds like a pun – only a short-sighted man ignores his face, especially his skin. At any age it is a man's face people notice first and at this age, whether he is handsome or not, it is this face that reflects his lifestyle, his apparent success or lack of it, and it is this face that shows all the signs of wear, tear and aging. So it makes sense to concentrate on keeping the head in as good a condition as possible for as long as possible. Short of resorting to cosmetic surgery, there may not be much a man can do if he does not like the aesthetic details of his face, or to remove the bags and wrinkles once they have set in but, nonetheless, with a minimum of effort on his part the face can look healthy and glowing with vitality and so project the impression that here is a fit man, full of energy, ready for action.

A face in prime condition helps get new work, new loves and better life. And taking care of the body as a whole is the correct insurance for the future. Routines are simple and based on cleanliness. None are costly.

Hair

Even if you are worried by a hairline that is receding or falling hair and a balding patch that could be increasing in size daily, taking care of your hair should not represent a problem. In fact the route to good hair is so simple that it seems impossible that so many men we see in public places should have such bad hair in such bad condition.

To get it right all you need is a good haircut to make the hair both manageable and flattering, and the correct shampoo. Some men may also need to use a conditioner occasionally, and for some, perming or colouring will work an additional, aesthetic wonder. Nothing beats a healthy diet for maintaining healthy hair once its condition is right.

But first the worrying problem, baldness.

Not all men go bald, nor will they. But for many men around their mid-thirties thinning hair becomes a problem with bald areas developing and after sixty, unless they are eunuchs, the majority of men will have hair that is noticeably thinner on the ground than when they were younger. (Men who are eunuchs since early boyhood never go bald, it appears, but once a man has started to lose his hair castration will not make it grow again. It may be something of a relief to many men to know that castration is not a cure.)

A considerable amount of baloney has been written about curing baldness. There is no cure. If there were no movie star would wear a toupé (Charlton Heston, Burt Reynolds and Sean Connery to name but three) and none would invest in costly, painful hair transplantation operations (Sinatra and Elton John).

Treatments carried out in hair clinics will certainly clear up scalp problems and keep the remaining hair in excellent condition but where the hair roots are dead (which is what baldness is, the dying off of roots) no amount of massage, potions, creams, injections and infra-red treatments will revive them and bring them growing back to life. The day a cure for baldness is medically proven the news will make international headlines (again, no pun intended) and the discoverer will make his fortune.

Unless a man loses his hair through trauma or illness, in which case the loss may only be temporary, all baldness is hereditary. This in the textbooks is known as MHB, male hereditary baldness. Every man inherits a growth pattern from the genes-dominant side of his family. His hair could be similar to his father's, or to that of his grandfather or great-grandfather on either the paternal or maternal side of the family. Which side he inherits from is a matter of luck and nothing can be done to change it.

The best solution to the problem is to come to terms with being bald, not to fight it, and to ask your barber or hairdresser to change the style of your cut. This is not so they can disguise the baldness however. You should never tug, grease, pull or borrow hair from the side of the head so that it covers the bald spot with whirling fronds. This kind of ridiculous trickery only looks like the camouflage it is and fools no one. It only heightens the impression that underneath there is a scalp as bald as a billiard ball.

This recommendation to change the style of the haircut is also right for men whose hair is noticeably thinner now than it was. Go to a stylist who can cut the hair into a balanced shape, closer to the head, so that the lie of the hair looks natural and the hair itself is manageable and trouble-free. A good cut will make the remaining hair look healthy and draw attention away from the balding area.

By and large the shorter the cut, the better the look. It gives the face new strength and dimension and creates a look that is individual. Men who grow their remaining hair longer than normal make their bald patch look worse. The contrast between hair and no-hair makes the patch doubly obvious.

If you cannot face life without some form of covering think hard before you consider surgery or before you invest in either a hairpiece or hairweaving. No matter how persuasively consultants talk nor how much you pay for the piece, both cover-up systems show. Which is preferable, showing a false head of hair or a balding patch? The choice is strictly personal but remember as you continue to lose hair so the hairpiece or weave will have to be changed and made larger.

As a dramatic alternative you could also consider shaving your head totally in the manner of Yul Brynner and Telly Savalas. It requires some bravery but if the shape of your head is good the shaven result can be effective. One eminent author with alopaecia has taken to doing so rather than face falling hair each day. His recommendation is that the bald head must be tanned to look right but he also points out that bald heads sunburn easily and feel the cold unless you take protection.

Generally most men benefit from a change of hairstyle after thirty-nine. There may be little wrong with the old cut but it is likely to be dull and a little out of touch. Too long at the back, for example, or bushy at the sides or with Seventies sideburns creeping down the cheeks. To get the newer cut may mean spending more money than usual but if you go to a reputable salon the cut will be natural, good-looking, individual and as the advertisement might say, well worth it.

Many men today have their hair lightly permed to give it extra texture and many with nondescript hair have it coloured or streaked. To get this kind of treatment right it must be carried out professionally and not at home with the do-it-yourself kits available from stores' counters. If you are worried about going grey have it coloured professionally and avoid using hair colour restorers. The colour these give is flat and unreal and under artificial light the hair often looks spinach green or aubergine. On most men greying hair looks distinguished and adds to, rather than detracts from, appearance. Many people are prematurely grey; the days when grey hair was a sign of age are long passed.

How many times you should wash your hair depends on lifestyle and where you live. In a city where pollution is a problem you will have to wash your hair more often than if you live in clean-air countryside. And if you play sport you should wash your hair after each game in order to keep it clean, glossy and healthy. Oily hair usually needs three washes a week; dry hair about every five days.

Obviously if you have dandruff you must use a dandruff shampoo. These contain either zinc pyrithione or selenium sulfide as active ingredients and so must be used according to manufacturers instructions on the label. If the shampoo containing pyrithione does not work for you switch to one with selenium sulfide. All dandruff shampoos have their active ingredients listed.

Where normal shampoos are concerned you have to experiment until you find a shampoo that suits your hair and leaves it in excellent condition. Cheap shampoos are inclined to be strong while the more expensive ones are better perfumed and more gentle. Most have detergent as their cleansing agent. A shampoo that is too strong will leave your hair feeling brittle and your scalp uncomfortably tight and it will strip the hair of its protection and the scalp of its natural oils. If the brand you use does not meet your demands switch brands until you find one that does.

There is little noticeable difference to be gained by using herbal shampoos or those with added ingredients like eggs or beer. These special ingredients are there to enhance the sales appeal of the product and are in minute quantities which, anyway, come off in the rinsing. However if you find you like using one of these shampoos and your hair looks and feels right as a result, stick with it.

Whichever shampoo you choose through experiment, it must make your hair look healthy and glossy and be good to the touch. The scalp must be clean without feeling tight, over-scrubbed or itchy. If your hair fails on one of these points you are using the wrong brand.

If you have fine or unmanageable hair try using protein-enriched or balsam shampoos as they are specially formulated to leave a slight residue on each hair shaft that will give the hair extra suppleness and body. Or you could try using a hair conditioner. These are prepared for hair that is brittle, dull or dry. Follow the instructions carefully. A conditioner used incorrectly can clog the scalp's pores and cause additional problems. Note: any man whose hair is already in good, healthy condition does not need either protein-enriched or balsam shampoos – nor conditioners.

To wash the hair properly there is a simple routine that should be followed. It is basic but many men get it wrong.

First, using the tips of the fingers massage the scalp for one minute by pressing down firmly and using a rotating motion. Do not scratch or use fingernails. This massage stimulates the scalp and helps blood flow through to feed the hair roots as well as relax tightness or tension and, most important, loosens grime or dead skin cells ready for washing.

Under tepid water – not hot – soak the hair and then work in a small amount of shampoo. Gently, as in the massage. Let the cleansing properties of the shampoo do their work. This washing should last one minute.

Rinse thoroughly.

If you feel the hair needs a second shampoo follow the same gentle routine. Again rinse thoroughly. Clean hair will squeak as it is rinsed so keep rinsing until it does.

Towelling the hair dry, continue to be gentle. Never rub violently but pat the hair and firmly massage the head so that the towel absorbs all the moisture. Then reshape the hair using fingers or a wide-toothed comb. If you finish off with a hairdryer keep the nozzle well away from the hair so that the hair is not cooked and, if you can, leave just a little moisture on the hair so that the final drying is natural. This will ensure the hair still has bounce to it rather than be stiff and tortured.

It has been noticed that many men wash their hair in water that is too hot (which over-stimulates the sebaceous glands and so makes the scalp greasier than it should be) and are rough-actioned with the towel when drying the hair. This may seem like a macho way to treat hair but it is also a sure way for pulling the hair out. So too is brushing. Never use a brush. For tidying the hair use a wide-toothed comb.

There is no doubt that balanced diet plays a vital role in the life of healthy hair; bad diet and poor nutrition contribute to dry and brittle hair problems and aggravate dandruff conditions.

To get the right balance of vitamins we need through food each week we should regularly eat small amounts of liver, fish, pulses, fresh fruit, and green vegetables like spinach. All these foods contain essential vitamin-B that strengthens the hair (and body). To get an extra boost of the vitamin most trichologists recommend patients to take a course of vitamin-B complex or yeast tablets. These are readily available at all health food stores or pharmacies.

The Face

Nothing short of cosmetic surgery and silicone injections can remove bags and wrinkles. In the process of aging the skin loses its elasticity and starts to sag or fold, and under the eyes bags form as little pads of fat force their way through the tissue beneath the skin. The older a man gets until he is sixty the more deeply etched the wrinkles appear to be and after that he may develop an additional skin problem, random pigmentation, where age-spots appear on the face or back of hands. These can be removed by special creams that contain bleaching agents.

All actors and movie stars take particular care of their faces whether they are known for their handsome looks or the character parts they play. Stars of the calibre of Paul Newman and Robert Redford are often seen visiting a well-known New York salon for facial treatments and many others the world over take equal care. How else could they keep their photogenic looks?

In fact taking care of the face is simple and does not demand that each of us visits a salon. All it requires is correct cleansing and moisturizing cream. Healthy diet, early nights, minimum alcohol and no tobacco or drugs also help improve the condition of the face. There is many a Hollywood luminary who neither smokes nor drinks and lives exclusively on health food produce purely so that the face remains intact.

Cleansing the face is a three-stage procedure.

The *first step* requires soap and water. With a good quality mild soap wash the face twice a day, morning and night.

For the *second step,* cleanse the face with an astringent lotion dabbed on a cottonball. Once a day, preferably in the evening, is sufficient. This is especially important on the greasy regions of the face like the forehead, the temples, the sides of the nose and behind the ears where grime caused by sweat forms. To see how much your face needs this kind of cleansing, try dabbing cologne or aftershave on to a cottonball and during the late evening cleanse your face with it. Examine the cottonball. It will be grease-covered. An astringent lotion specially designed for this task will be doubly effective and half as costly.

This done, the *third step* is to apply a non-greasy moisturizer to the skin to lubricate it. Moisturizers protect and soften the surface of the skin from the outside. Apply some after washing the face and after deep cleansing. A moisturizer can be used all over the face with special emphasis around the eyes and where dry patches appear to be. Like an aftershave balm, a moisturizer can be used after shaving in order to stop tautness or irritation.

Astringents and moisturizers are easily found in stores and pharmacies and men's toiletry companies knowing that many men are shy about buying products packaged for women – and knowing good business when they see it – have formulated identical products for men. The ingredients and contents are much the same as women's lines but the wrapping is more masculine.

There are a number to choose from. Aramis, Saint Laurent, Roger & Gallet, for example, and Clinique, the American company with a broad international base, offers a wide range of practical skin products that includes soap, scruffing lotion (their name for an astringent lotion), moisturizer and extras like a face scrub for a once a week deeper cleansing, and a shampoo. The Clinique range is unperfumed and allergy-tested and designed to be essentially masculine.

As cosmeticians always say, only a foolish man does not take care of his skin. It takes about one week following this three-stage routine for improvements to be markedly noticeable. Blemishes like spots soon clear up and the skin appears healthy and glowing.

Obviously wrinkles and bags remain, but as a result of the grooming care they seem less obvious in their healthy surroundings.

A suntan also helps a face look good but it has been established that there is a link between too much sun and skin cancer. And on a less serious note, too much sun prematurely ages the skin by drying it out. So in strong sunshine always use a protective suntan cream on the face and afterwards cleanse the face properly; then, the face clean, apply either an aftersun cream or a basic moisturizer to restore lubrication and protection to the skin's surface.

While concentrating on the face any man who wears spectacles should consider whether as part of his new approach to life he should switch to contact lenses. Correctly chosen glasses can enhance a man's face and give it the extra character it may be lacking but sometimes lenses make for a total transformation for the better. Often a face will look considerably younger.

Bleary, red and bloodshot eyes on the other hand make a man look worse and hung up on drink, drugs and late nights. Should the redness be caused by allergy or infection it must be treated immediately by a doctor as eye problems of this nature can lead to serious complications. Red-eye caused by late nights, drink or smoking can be rectified by pharmacy eyedrops.

The Body

Again, care is purely a matter of total cleanliness: a tub or shower, warm water, and a soap wash with special care being taken of the underarms, genital and anal areas and the feet. Antiperspirants and deodorants will ensure the body remains odour-free for a number of hours and if you feel like smelling nice you could add a dash of cologne. It is also essential that having followed this routine properly you change shirt, underwear and socks daily too. Clean clothes are as much a part of total cleanliness as clean skin.

Many men skip on the routines that keep their hands in good condition and the state of their feet up to scratch. Bad hands and smelly feet are signs of a man who has let himself go.

Badly kept hands ruin a man's appearance and it is often claimed that when seeking a job poor nails can alienate a prospective employer and make him take a longer look at other candidates. Any man can take care of his hands by gently scrubbing them with a brush and then, with nailfile and scissors, manicuring them. Cuticle remover cream will keep the surrounds looking clear and handcream will keep the hands supple.

The same sort of care applies to feet too; a good scrub with a brush and a pedicure with nailfile and scissors. Poor foot care and dirty socks are the breeding ground for athletes foot. Feet respond well to scrubbing and can be talcummed or dusted with anti-fungal powder before socks are worn.

c. Diet: Or Eating Sensibly

Nutrition experts and the medical profession agree: men in the Western world eat too much fat and fatty foods. Not only does this kind of food contain high counts of calories that turn to fat if we don't burn up enough through exercise, but it also causes high concentrations of fatty substances, cholesterol, in the bloodstream and so puts the heart at risk..

Therefore as a means to survival nothing is better than a diet that sticks to the rules of sensible eating. You look better, feel better, and have a body that responds better to its environment. By eating sensibly you cut out useless foods and cut down on the risks of heart problems, strokes and high blood pressure. Cut out fatty foods and automatically you help your heart.

The following are the rules of sensible eating – not to be confused with the rules of dieting to lose weight, which follow.

Do not eat fatty meats like sausage, salami, mortadella, pork and duck and avoid all meat fat including the fine slivers of fat ringing roast beef.

Avoid all fried foods as they soak up quantities of fat. If your family insist on a once-a-week fry-up either do not eat it or insist the food is fried only in a small amount of vegetable oil – never dripping or meat fats.

Unless your taste buds rebel switch to margarine or low-cholesterol spreads instead of butter which is high in cholesterol. If you must eat butter do so only in moderation.

Say No to cream.

Cut down on cheese as it is rich in animal fat. Go easy on milk.

Eat no more than three eggs a week.

Use only a little salt especially if already you have high blood pressure problems. Beware of the high salt content in most convenience foods, tinned or frozen.

Cut out sugar. This means sweets, cakes, biscuits, chocolate, ice cream (which is also high in fats) and colas and soft drinks. If you crave sweetness eat fruit.

Apart from the items listed in the rules above you can eat anything you like but when it comes to bread, pasta, rice and potatoes eat them only in moderation as they are high in carbohydrates, therefore fattening.

A meal without fatty foods should not represent a problem. Try fish or chicken instead of meat (chicken skin should be avoided as it is fatty). And insist on grilled food rather than fried. Go easy on cheese. Although many slimmers think cheese is an ideal dietary aid it is rich in animal fats and unless eaten sparingly may contribute to putting on weight rather than shedding it.

Eat as many green vegetables and salads as you like. Not only are they an excellent source of vitamins and minerals but they also supply the essential fibre the system needs to keep it functioning efficiently.

The Ideal Weight

These are the desirable weights calculated on statistics gathered in the United States by life assurance companies. Height is measured in bare feet; weight in minimum indoor clothing.

It is permissible to be 4 lbs (1.8kg) above or below this mean average without being considered either over or under-weight.

Height	small frame		medium frame		large frame	
	lbs	kg	lbs	kg	lbs	kg
5ft 4in (162cm)	125	56.7	133	60.3	143	64.9
5ft 5in (165cm)	128	58	136	61.7	147	66.6
5ft 6in (167cm)	132	59.9	140	63.5	151	68.5
5ft 7in (170cm)	136	61.7	145	65.8	156	70.8
5ft 8in (172cm)	140	63.5	149	67.6	160	72.6
5ft 9in (175cm)	145	65.8	153	69.4	164	74.4
5ft 10in (177cm)	149	67.6	157	71.2	169	76.7
5ft 11in (180cm)	153	69.4	162	73.5	174	78.9
6ft (183cm)	157	71.2	166	75.3	178	80.7
6ft 1in (185cm)	161	73	171	77.6	183	83
6ft 2in (188cm)	165	74.9	176	79.8	188	85.2
6ft 3in (190cm)	169	76.6	181	82	193	87.5
6ft 4in (193cm)	173	78.5	286	84.4	198	89.8

Slimming

To lose weight by dieting you have to cut down drastically on the amount you eat and the numbers of calories or carbohydrates each dish contains. While many men claim instant success following the basic calorie-count diets and others swear by the well-publicized, money-spinning diets that are printed in books like the F-Plan and Scarsdale diets, there is unfortunately no one regimen that takes short-cuts or guarantees a man will lose excess poundage without his total attention, application and willpower. The bad news is that after the mid-thirties shedding weight is more of a problem than it would have been in the mid-twenties, so a man has to be total in his dedication in order to make the scales show less.

Very fit sportsmen burn up their excess calories through their regular exercise and, in fact, sport being an ideal aid to slimming, it is essential that anyone dieting take some exercise too. Not only will this help shed the poundage quicker but it firms and tones up the body at the same time. A twenty-minute swim twice a week will do nicely.

It has been reckoned that a Mr Average doing a sedentary job needs something in the region of 2,400 calories a day (more if physical labour is involved) and on a health farm as a dramatic crash diet they may suggest 500 calories a day as a sure-fire, but supervised, way to weight loss. Less drastically they may also recommend a less severe diet of 1,000 or 1,500 calories for one week which is kinder to the metabolism and not such a debilitating shock to the system. These sets of diets must be supervised.

To burn up one pound of weight it has been calculated you need to burn 3,500 calories above your daily requirement. The following table is generally used to indicate the approximate numbers of calories a man will burn up during motion or sport.

120 to 150 calories per hour:
walking at 1 mph

150 to 240 calories
walking at 2 mph

240 to 300 calories
walking at 3 mph
bicycling at 6 mph
bowling

300 to 360 calories
bicycling at 8 mph
golf, carry clubs yourself
rowing at 3 mph
riding
swimming at .25 mph
tennis, playing doubles

360 to 420 calories
walking at 4 mph
bicycling at 10 mph
roller skating
ice skating

420 to 480 calories
walking at 5 mph
bicycling at 11 mph
tennis, singles

480 to 600 calories
jogging at 5 mph
bicycling at 12 mph

600 to 660 calories
running at 6 mph
bicycling at 13 mph
squash
skiing

900 calories
running at 10 mph

If most men make a point of eating less, skipping second helpings and avoiding fatty foods they will lose weight gradually. There are three diets listed here, one a crash diet based on calorie counting and two with only rules to follow that are ideal for the man who because of his way of life cannot guarantee to be able to follow a strict regimen of meals. These two, the *No-Sugar No-Flour* diet and the *Good and the Bad* diet will help shed weight not dramatically quickly, but gradually.

The No-Sugar No-Flour Diet:
There is one rule only: eat nothing that is made with, of, or contains either flour or sugar. Ever.

This cuts out many more foods than would appear obvious on first consideration. Sauces usually contain flour, so do dishes like soufflés and casseroles so it is not only items like bread, pasta and biscuits that have to be avoided. And sugar is one of the major ingredients of many convenience foods, from soups to stews.

Learn to check out ingredients of every dish and go easy on alcohol with this diet. Too much will weaken willpower as well as activate the taste buds so that they yearn for both sweet foods and carbohydrates.

On this diet most men lose three to four pounds in the first week. The rate of loss is more gradual after that but it is, nonetheless, an effective diet.

The Good-and-the-Bad Diet:
The rules: Eat as much as you like from the *Good* list.
Follow instructions on the *Go Slow* list. Eat no more each day than amounts shown.
Eat *none* of the foods on the *Bad* list.

Good—

proteins: White fish, seafood.
Lean meat only: beef, lamb, pork, liver, kidney, heart, sweetbreads, tripe, lean ham free of preservative, rabbit, venison.
Chicken, turkey, pheasant, quail.
Cottage cheese, goat cheese, fetta, mozzarella.

fats: Vegetable oils (but not for frying).

carbohydrates: Artichokes, asparagus, broccoli, cabbage, cauliflower, celery, endive, kale, lettuce, spinach. All salad greens, tomatoes, peppers, cucumber, marrow, aubergine, onions.

		Citrus: lemons, grapefruit, oranges, tangerines. Bilberries, cranberries, gooseberries, raspberries, strawberries. Black or red currants. Figs, apricots, peaches, grapes, cantaloupe, mango, papaya, pineapple, apples, pears, plums, cherries.
	liquids:	Black coffee, black tea, low-calorie drinks. Skimmed milk.
Go Slow—	*proteins:*	Eggs, cheese (100g per day). Duck, goose, water fowl (100g).
	fats:	Milk (0.3 litre), butter (25g), margarine (25g).
	carbohydrates:	Carrots (100g), turnips (100g), beetroot (100g), potatoes (100g), ½ avocado, 1 banana, pulses, (100g).
	starch:	Brown rice (100g), pasta (100g), wholegrain bread (2 slices), cereals (100g).
	liquids:	Alcohol (one measure). Soups (.25 litre)

NB: It is important to stick to the measurements listed in this section: 100 grams (3.5 oz) is a small amount.

Bad—	*sugars:*	All sweets, chocolate, spreads, sauces, glucose, biscuits, cakes, pies. Jams, marmalades. Canned or preserved fruits.
	Starch:	White bread. White flours, refined grains, white rice, flour-based sauces. Tinned, root and pod vegetables. Nuts.
	fats:	Cream, sauces, bottle sauces, ketchup and relish. Processed meats, sausages.

Calorie-Control Diet

This is the way to reduce weight effectively and quickly. Once the ideal weight is reached it will be easier to maintain because as well as cutting out forbidden foods this diet retrains the appetite and palate to enjoy healthy foods.

Because calorie count is reduced to 1,400 calories each day, this diet should only be followed for fourteen days.

Breakfast: ½ grapefruit or glass unsweetened fruit juice
1 egg (not fried) or lean meat
1 piece wholemeal toast
thin spread margarine or butter
coffee or tea (no sugar but artificial sweetener acceptable)

Lunch: 100g lean meat *or* poultry or fish (not fried)
fresh cooked vegetables *or* salad
1 piece wholemeal bread
1 fruit in season
coffee or tea (no sugar)

Dinner: 100g lean meat *or* poultry *or* fish
fresh cooked vegetables
mixed salad (lemon or low-calorie dressing only)
cheese (50g)
1 fruit in season
coffee or tea (no sugar)

NB: No more than .25 skimmed milk each day. As much water or no-calorie drink as you like. No alcohol.

The Restaurant Hurdle

For any man whose business life involves eating out constantly in restaurants it is vital to learn how to survive so that you can comfortably eat your way across a menu. This way you do not upset your host – or guest – and you do not compromise your diet by eating the wrong things. It also saves having to talk about dieting and so appearing a diet-bore.

To start: choose a dish that is light and simple, one without a sauce. A thin soup or consommé, perhaps, or crudités, mixed salad, grapefruit, soused herrings or rollmop. Italian dishes like prosciutto melone or mozzarella and tomato are fine too if you are not strictly counting calories.

Avoid pasta, rice dishes, thick soups, prawn or shrimp cocktail (because of the sauce), any fried fish like whitebait, paté and egg mayonnaise. Skip any dish with cheese or thick sauce.

Main course: this is easy ground as most restaurants will serve grilled fish or steak. But if this becomes monotonous select from other dishes carefully, choosing lean meat or fish dishes first or salads with cold meats that do not include sausage. Of course, nothing fried. Enjoy all the vegetables that are in season unless they are fried or come under a sauce. No French fries but a small portion of boiled potatoes is fine, or one small baked potato.

Beware of selecting pies or casseroles because of their fatty meat content and the flour that will have been used for thickening the sauces.

Sweet: skip icecream and puddings. If you must have something sweet choose a piece of fresh fruit or fresh fruit salad (no cream). Unless you are on a strict diet a small piece of cheese with a couple of crackers is a good substitute.

Alcohol: should be kept down to a minimum. Perhaps a vodka with soda water not tonic before the meal and only a glass of white wine to follow. To quench the thirst and keep the consumption of wine to a minimum also drink mineral water.

d. Dressing Successfully

Many men get it wrong. Some dress badly because they think clothes are unimportant, some leave the buying of their clothes to their wives and others, we know, dress-young as they struggle to keep up with the gang.

Obviously around M-M time dressing in an odd-ball way is fine if you are an eccentric or perhaps a painter or sculptor but it is hardly constructive if you still want to get ahead and be successful. With the ego already worried a man needs all the help he can get from his outer trappings. Just as his face and hair care contribute to confidence, so the choice of clothes should help bolster career and life in general.

The truth is that no matter how much a man may swear he is disinterested in clothes, deep inside he knows he would like to be well-dressed and admired for the way he dresses. Often the problem is simply that he does not know where to start and at around forty it seems to him that every shop window is full of clothes designed exclusively for the fashion-plate whose age must be twenty-five.

To succeed with minimum trouble all it needs is a few guidelines and one important recommendation that will undoubtedly be repeated: at this age, spend more not less – but buy less. Inexpensive clothes may look fine but on a man around forty they look what they are, inexpensive and inexpensively made. They may be fun and cheap but they rarely flatter.

Very expensive clothes may not be the answer either even if they have an illustrious designer's name emblazoned on the label. High prices and famous names are not necessarily a guarantee of good design and where clothes are concerned more often than not, unless the clothes are made from expensive fabrics like cashmere or silk, designer label clothes are mostly designed with the money-spending twenty-five to thirty-five age group in mind.

The answer lies in looking for quality of make, fabric and design. Window-shop first. Look around. See what is available in the major stores and quality establishments before making your selection. Go for quality allied to style and this way the clothes you choose should be good fashion, look good, flatter and, a nice point, last a long time. Good quality shows and goes only slowly out of fashion.

If you were known in your earlier years as something of a snappy dresser there is nothing wrong in being one still in your forties. The difference now is that you are not setting trends for the young set but for your contemporaries. (No matter how you think of yourself, to the young set you are just about middle-aged. So ignore the way they dress.)

Recommendation number two: dress for your contemporaries and (why not?) be known for your excellent style in clothes. This does not mean being safely dressed like a city banker and wearing nothing but navy blue suits though there is a lot to be said for navy blue suits, nor do you have to be the first with each season's new colours as they come out. See yourself as a Born Again Trendy. Like a born-again-Christian who rediscovers Christianity, rediscover stylish clothes. Take advice if you are unsure from people whose judgement you respect. Look for clothes that suit you and the way you live.

The easiest way to start the change is by looking for faults in the clothes you already have and start slowly to replace them. Ignore all your contemporaries who you know dress badly but compare yourself with your circle of friends. Are there many who dress better than you? How do they get it right? Is it their clothes that are better, or their physique?

Ruthlessly start throwing out clothes that have seen their day – regardless of what you paid for them when they were new. If you still have flared pants, psychadelic print shirts, kipper ties, platform-sole shoes, jackets with narrow shoulders and wide lapels, lock them away safely in a trunk if you cannot face parting with them but don't wear them. Slowly rebuild your wardrobe with clothes that will not let you down. In the same way you might consider changing the shape of your spectacles or your haircut, think about changing the cut of your clothes.

Begin with the basics. A suit that is up-to-date is vital, so too are a sports jacket in a good tweed, a toning pair of wellcut pants, half-a-dozen shirts and two pairs of shoes. Having established this minimum foundation start adding. Choose clothes that are useful and practical within your life pattern. Be selective.

Dressing Successfully: The Ten Commandments

1: Keep up to date

Do not expect your clothes to last indefinitely. If they do, wear them for gardening or clearing out the garage and not for dinner or to the office.

Do not take the changes in fashion too seriously, you do not *have* to dress like the pages of a fashion magazine. Leave that to others.

However, look around and keep an open eye for the new clothes in the better shops and stores so that even if you are not buying at least you know what is right. Look at the cut of jackets, the lapel widths, the waistline, the buttoning, the vent. And the cut of trousers, shape of shirt collars, width of ties. Spot the details of the minute changes in style by seeing them in the shops rather than take your influence from footballers or comedians on television most of whom are out of touch. Know what is right.

Make sure that any bargains you spot in this year's sales do not turn out to be last year's bargains still on sale.

2: Choose classic clothes

When in doubt play safe but not dull.

If you want to look good nothing beats clothes that are styled along traditional lines in a classic mould. For example the best raincoats that rarely go out of fashion are trenchcoats, the sort that Humphrey Bogart wore to perfection in movies, the sort that Aquascutum and Burberry have made world famous. These are classic raincoats.

And equally classic are Shetland wool sweaters with crew necks, Oxford cloth shirts, plaid shirts, cords, flannels and brogues. The changes in style that affect them are only minimal. Because their design has a timeless quality, classic clothes are good investment.

3: Wear the right clothes for what you are doing

It does not matter much what you wear for digging the garden but almost anywhere else it does. People judge a man by how he dresses, socially or at work. Select what you wear with care; never be sloppy.

This means that you should think hard before you buy an item and visualize when, where and how you are going to wear this particular item. Never buy needlessly.

Going to work, take time to put the right shirt and tie together with the right suit or jacket and pants. Going to dinner dress with the same exactness whether the dinner is formal or informal. And going to the beach do not look as if your clothes have come out of the jumble bag or are a relic of your schooldays. If you can get your clothes right not only do you look right but you feel right.

4: Spend more not less

Yes; but in the long run this should be thrift rather than extravagance. Quality clothes are made better and last longer.

Perhaps the point to this commandment is that it is not an order, nor even encouragement, to go out and spend a fortune. It is a recommendation that all you do is spend a little more than you would normally consider doing in order to achieve the kind of style detail and quality of manufacture that is now your due. Only people in their twenties can get away with wearing cheap clothes.

This commandment applies especially to major investment items like suits where only the best will do, but you cannot go far wrong considering the same advice for all items of clothing, shirts and shoes in particular. A man is still judged by his shirt and shoes – in elegant circles the sure sign of a well-dressed man.

Be wary however when considering name-designer clothes. Never buy them simply because a famous name is on the label or because the salesman tells you they are making an important fashion statement.

Just because a designer's name features in the international magazines this does not mean that the cut of his clothes will automatically fit you or suit you as well as similar ones from other less known companies. Each designer's basic pattern differs, so when shopping apply the same set of rules about fit, comfort and use as you would when looking at clothes from the less famous.

There are many illustrious names to choose from today, some extremely high in quality and style, and, whether the name is Armani, Cerruti, Lauren, Saint Laurent or one of the others in this elite league, the best investments from their ranges are usually in their selections of classic suits, jackets and outerwear. A suit may seem to cost an inordinately high sum of money but not only will its cut and quality be to the highest standards, it will look its worth and make you feel good when wearing it.

5: Be colourful

Never buy drab-coloured clothes. Steer clear of dull shades of lovat, stone, putty and pale green. And unless you are confident you look good in pale grey and yellow avoid them too. In drab colours most men look drab.

The solution is simple. Go for strong, rich colours: reds, blues, greens and brown. Unless you are partial to and look good in fire engine red, sunflower yellow and burning orange put primary colours on the no-go list too.

Start from the outside. Select suits in fabrics that are in strong shades of navy, grey or brown. These colours may not be breaking new ground but they are the essential foundations to an elegant wardrobe and not only do they make a man look good (and, most likely, slimmer), they are a good foil for showing off shirts and ties.

For most formal occasions – and interviews – nothing beats a white shirt and a subtly colourful silk tie, and most men can never go far wrong wearing a blue shirt either. But if this is too routine, look into the selections of shirts that are patterned and select those that have a clean-looking background. Avoid creams, beige, lilac and dove grey as they do nothing for the appearance and if they don't make the face look drawn, haggard, ill or tired, make the man look as if he is trying too hard to keep up with fashion – and failing.

If you are unsure about whether a shirt colour suits you take it to a mirror, hold it up to your face. You would try on a jacket, a sweater and even a swimsuit so why not hold a shirt up to your face in front of a mirror? Judge for yourself.

As for sweaters, look for those that are maroon, dark green, navy, rust and all rich shades of blue, in plains or patterns, so that they can be worn stylishly with flannels or coloured cords. If you are partial to the brighter colours wear them as polo shirts, sports shirts or ties.

The final effect of this rich colouring highlighted by white or a limited amount of bright colours may seem unadventurous or, initially, traditional. But the colours are effective and make for simple elegance which, after forty, is what most of us need unless we are headed for the beach – which is another story.

Rich colours work; drab colours do not.

6: Be (classically) adventurous

Do not fall back on the old styles simply because they are the kind of clothes you have always worn. See what is new; try them on. Find out if the new styles will work for you and the kind of life you lead. Ignore items that make a bold fashion statement but examine the new arrivals – jackets, cords, lightweight suits, cardigans, polo shirts, anything – in the better stores and boutiques.

If you have not already done so, try on soft tweed sports coats, the new-shape trousers, trenchcoats, the new sweaters and suits that cost far more than you would pay normally. And think when looking at them how, when and where you can wear them and consider if they can be worn in more than one way or up-date something you already own. Clothes should be versatile. A leather jacket, for example, probably costs a small fortune so you should make sure if you are buying one that you can wear it two ways: casually over a polo shirt or sweater and, more formally, with a shirt and tie. Try for garments that are practical as well as good-looking so that you can get reasonable mileage out of them.

It is by being far-sighted and adventurous with your clothes and by successfully mixing and matching shirts, sweaters, jackets and pants that your clothes begin to work for you. You will need less clothes and people will notice you for your stylish changes.

When revising your wardrobe select clothes knowing that they will work well with the other good clothes you already have.

7: Buy the right size

Just because you wore a size 15 shirt and size 38 jacket when you were eighteen it does not mean you will still do so at twenty-eight or thirty-eight. No matter how fit you are and how close your weight is now to that of your twenties, your body will have changed both its shape and measurement. The neck will probably have thickened, the waistline certainly, and the bottom will have sagged just that little bit. It is a sad fact of life that most men's stomachs and waistlines will change even if they are careful about diet and what they eat. At this age only constant exercise keeps a waistline slim and a stomach flat.

The most common fault in dressing is the fit of the clothes yet it is one fault that should never happen nor be allowed to. For unless you shop exclusively in chain stores where you may have a problem, all shops readily exchange an item if it is the wrong size and most shops and boutiques expect to carry out alterations in order to get a perfect fit whether it is a matter of shortening a jacket's sleeves or taking in the seat and waistline of a pair of trousers. Many neighbourhood dry cleaners also carry out simple, inexpensive alterations.

The worst faults are with shirt collars (too big, loose, gaping at the front), shirt waistlines (too small, buttons straining over the stomach) and perhaps worst of all, trousers that not only hang half-mast and flap around the ankles but sag baggily in the seat. Clothes that fit this badly do so either because they are the wrong size or because they are badly in need of alterations or because they are cut for a body type other than the one that is wearing them.

If you have any doubts about your own measurements ask a salesman to check. And remember that although a size 40 jacket may in theory be your correct size, it may not fit you as well as it should because the size 40 block being used does not conform to your own body type and measurements. Try another manufacturer's size 40 and the fit may be perfect. Seek out companies that make along the lines of your shape.

Whether the clothes are up-to-the minute in fashion or not, fit matters and faults caused by ill-fit illustrate either a man who has no idea about dressing well or a wife/mother/lover who buys her man the wrong clothes.

Any woman who sees her man's clothes fitting him badly should do something about it and rectify the faults. And if you are the man whose clothes fit badly you have only yourself to blame. You are wearing the clothes.

8: Avoid fancy dress

Clothes you see being worn in pop shows on television by rock stars or in discos and clubs by young swingers are fun and look great on the guys wearing them, but once you are over twenty-five resist the temptation to dress like them. It may work for the older men of pop like Rod Stewart and on a beach holiday it may be fun to dress ethnic or like the rest of the gang on the beach, but after forty these clothes can make you look as if you are dressed for a carnival party. Or, as bad, as if you are dressing-young.

If you have any doubts or think the clothes might be too young, too fashionable or too amusing, do not wear them.

9: Keep clothes clean

Nothing gives a clearer picture of an unsuccessful man or contributes more to the impression of a man whose life is going slowly downhill and falling apart than dirty clothes. Or clothes that permanently look crumpled, creased or un-pressed.

No man today can complain of having a problem keeping his clothes in good order as excellent cleaning facilities exist in every neighbourhood. Suits can be cleaned and retextured, trousers pressed, sweaters freshened. And at home shirts can be properly washed and pressed and shoes cleaned. The moment a stitch unfastens or a heel looks worn shoes must be taken to a cobbler.

Besides looking better because of the care and attention, clean clothes will last longer. At the end of each season clothes should be cleaned and then put away wrapped until they are needed. This is particularly important with winter clothes that will hang for six months before they are worn again.

10: Look after the body

Clothes may maketh the man but the best of clothes and appearance can be ruined by a man who is physically a mess, untidy or unfit.

A major part of getting it right and dressing successfully comes through being groomed, no matter which style you choose to express yourself. You can wear formal clothes in the manner of a high-powered executive or dress in the liberated manner of an advertising agency art director, or dress somewhere in between in an individual look, but to get it right not only must the clothes be clean but so too must the body wearing them. A well-cut suit can mask certain physical faults but it cannot hide the fact that the man beneath is slovenly. And where physical fitness helps with posture only careful grooming from hair to fingernails completes the successful image of a man going places in life.

No man can consider himself well-dressed – nor will anyone else – if his body is not cared for, head to toe.

e. Fitness and Exercise

There are some unmistakable and easily recognisable signs around the age of forty that show a body is in urgent need of exercise. Face a mirror naked. Is the body quite what it should be? How about the waist, slightly thicker than it was? Is there an even, fleshy layer of extra covering running around the waist and across the lower back? Does the chest look marginally thinner with the pectorals less evident? Are the shoulders beginning to round and stoop? And how does the stomach look in profile?

Consider too: are you stiff when you wake in the mornings? Having trouble running to catch a bus and climbing stairs? Feel listless or permanently tired? Not getting enough sleep? Sex life not what it was? Still smoking?

Unless you have recently been ill or are under doctor's orders, it is never too late to start taking some form of exercise – mild rather than violent. With the imminent arrival of middle age and with old age around the corner, the only way to face up to the future is by being as fit and healthy as possible. Of course we must not confuse being fit with being healthy. Although they both contribute to the same good condition, being fit means being able to sustain a good level of physical activity, and being healthy means being free of disease.

The reasons for taking some form of exercise are obvious. Not only do you look better and feel better, but you enjoy better health as the exercise strengthens the heart, lungs, circulation and muscles.

If you are already playing sport or working out regularly the recommendation to take exercise is unnecessary and only confirms what you already know from experience: being fit pays off. But for others this recommendation is worth heeding. What it does not mean in this context, however, is training the body until it is rippling with muscles and high definition although that sort of body is still within reach if you are dedicated enough to train seriously and go to a qualified instructor at a gymnasium with equipment like Nautilus. But at this age what you should have is a good-looking body with trim physique, upright posture and an appearance of being many years younger. This is the kind of body that performs well in everyday life. And sexually.

As a means of survival you can also consider taking up the menopausal sport of jogging if you are already close to being fit and sure that you are not going to drop down dead as some men have through weak heart and over-exertion, and, if you are prepared to risk sprains, back trouble, strained muscles, dog bites and traffic accidents. Besides firming the body jogging strengthens the heart and lungs, but before starting out make sure you buy good quality jogging shoes with thick well-cushioned soles. Pounding the hard pavements severely taxes the resilience of forty-year-old joints and sinews. And start slowly. Jogging is not racing, it is a long run simply for the fitness and pleasure it gives.

Squash and tennis are good fitness sports most men have access to but many doctors regard swimming as the best exercise readily available because not only does every muscle in the body have to perform, the heart and lungs have to work rhythmically too as they build up the body into an essentially fit machine. (To swim as exercise means a minimum of twenty minutes at a good pace, rather than leisurely dipping, three times a week.) Golf, the archetypal middle-aged man's sport, offers little exercise value unless you are carrying your own clubs.

The surest way to fitness without straining yourself is by following a planned routine on a gymnasium floor but if you feel you do not look too great stripped for action and cannot face the competition of fitter bodies, exercise at home. See the exercises that follow. *Fitness Plan x 3* has been devised by London instructors whose interest is restoring fitness to men who over the years have lost it. The exercises must be repeated three times a week – hence the 3 in the title – and they must be taken gradually, building up the repetitions as the body becomes fitter.

Please note: if you have any reservations about your health or recently have had an operation consult your doctor first before embarking on the Plan. Never take unnecessary risks. These exercises may look simple and be easy to perform but they are nonetheless taxing routines designed to stretch, strain and firm up the whole body.

Until you can gauge how fit you are, take the routines slowly. Each session should last in the region of fifteen minutes. Never exercise if you have a cold, or are ill, tired, under the influence of drink or drugs, or in a cold room. Should you feel faint or dizzy while exercising, stop.

Fitness Plan × 3

To re-condition the body.

This is a basic plan designed for men around 40 who are currently taking little or no exercise. It will improve strength, endurance and posture while concentrating on toning up the abdomen, waist, legs and shoulders. One exercise is specifically designed to improve the efficiency of heart and lungs.

These are exercises suitable for the fit and the not-so-fit but if you find the going hard, build up to the numbers of recommended repetitions slowly. Within a few weeks you should be able to handle all the exercises comfortably. If, however, you find you are coasting through them effortlessly, these exercises may not be doing you as much good as they should because without exertion the body will not strengthen. The solution: increase the number of repetitions of each routine and concentrate on those that you find most difficult.

The time these routines should take is about fifteen minutes each session. Never rush at the routines nor work out to the point of total exhaustion. Your speed and exertion should be moderate and constant so that the body builds up muscle and strength and you feel good after the workout.

Note: if you feel dizzy during the routine, stop. If you have any doubt about your fitness or have recently had an operation consult your doctor before embarking on the Fitness Plan.

Improvements in body tone should be apparent within four or five weeks. For best results there must be three workouts each week.

1. The Warm-Up

These are compulsory exercises that must be carried out before you start on the Plan's routines in order to limber the body in preparation for the exercises that follow. All the routines concentrate on improving mobility.

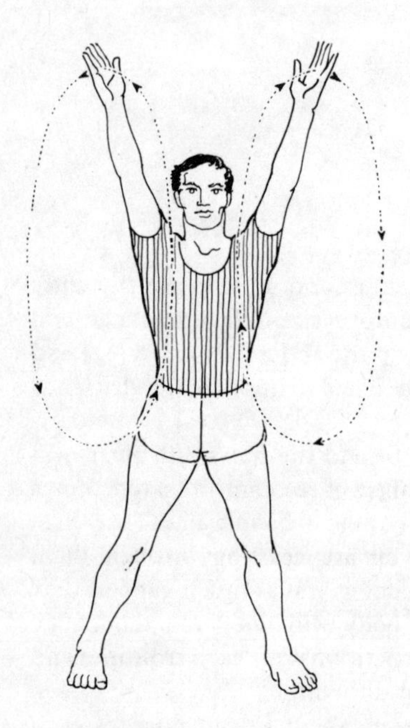

a: arm circling

position:

Feet shoulder width apart, arms at side, face forward.

action:

In controlled movement, not fast, circle both straight arms forward, up, over, backwards, in a windmill rotation.

repetition:

Circle 20 backwards, 20 forward.

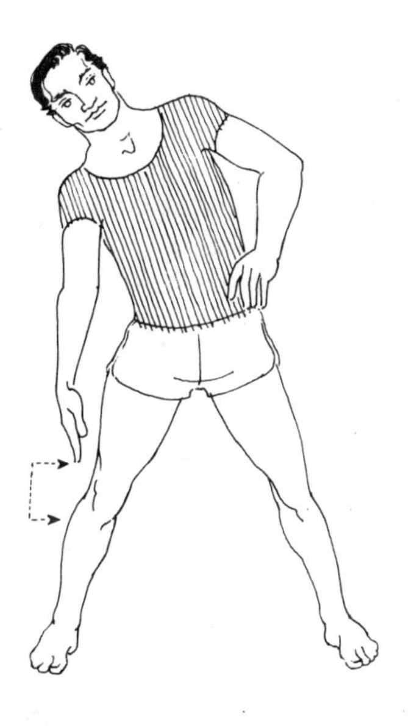

b: side bends with push

position:

Feet shoulder-width apart, face forward. Left hand to waist, right hand along side of body.

action:

In controlled easy motion bend to right, the hand reaching the knee, then push down harder so fingers reach lower, 6 inches at least. Straighten up. Change sides: right hand to waist, left hand along side of body. Bend left, reach, push hard, straighten. Repeat routines right and left. Note: action must be carried out bending only from waist, legs firm, face forward.

repetition:

Alternating, 10 each side. Speed should be moderate in continuous, non-stop motion.

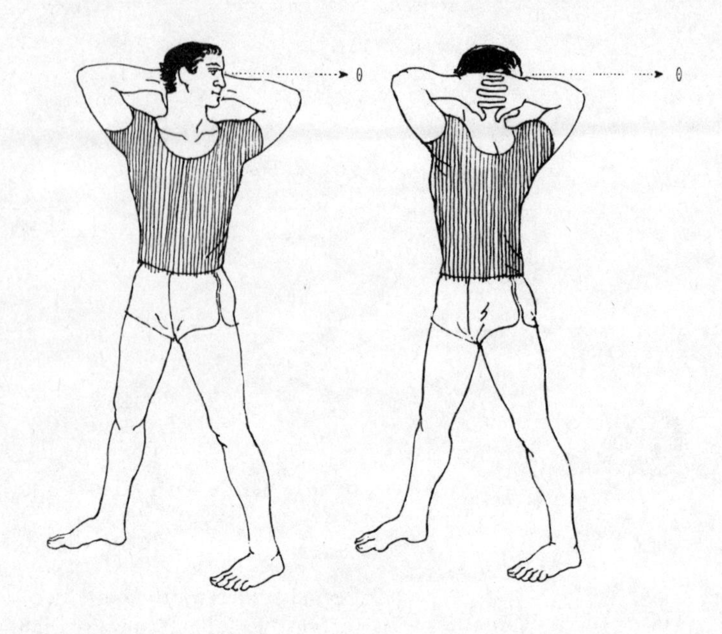

c: trunk rotating

position:

Feet shoulder width apart. Face forward with hands interlocked at nape of neck. Elbows straight out at sides.

action:

With feet firmly placed pointing forward and without turning hips or moving legs, rotate torso from the waist. To make sure you rotate fully select a fixed point on the wall behind you and ensure that as you twist in each direction so you can focus on it. To control the rotation it helps to thrust your hips in the opposite direction to the twist. (If you twist left, thrust right. Twist right, thrust left).

repetition:

15 each way. Speed moderate, eyes meeting focus point on each twist.

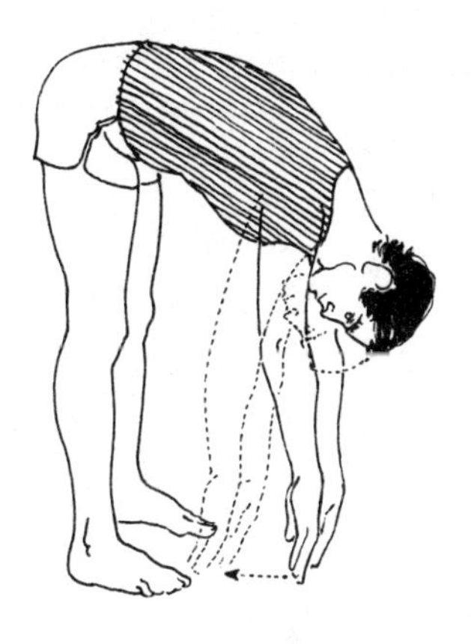

d: toe touching (with bounce)

position:

Feet slightly apart, arms at sides.

action:

Lock knees so legs remain straight. In deep toe-touching motion reach for ground in front of toes and in continuing motion bounce once to reach ground between open feet. Straighten up to start position.

repetition:

10 to 15 times.

Note: as you become fitter, so you can increase the number of repetitions to the warm-up exercises. However for increased fitness (as opposed to mobility), consider increasing the repetitions of the exercises that follow.

2. The Fitness Routine

a: sit-ups or leg-raisers

(Both are for stomach control but if you cannot manage a sit-up or have a back problem then the equally effective leg-raiser routine is for you).

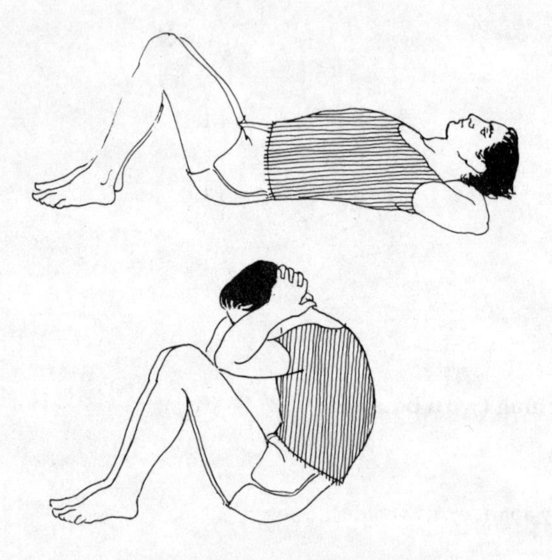

sit-ups

position:

Lie on floor, flat on back, knees bent. Clasp hands at back of head.

action:

Without jerking the body, sit up slowly and touch the knees with your elbows. Lower body gently to flat position.
This exercise can be carried out initially with feet placed under a retaining piece of furniture until you are strong enough to lift without a counterweight.

repetition:

If 5 is no problem, go for 10. Stick to 10 until you are fully fit before increasing to 15 and then 20.

leg-raisers

position:

Lie on back, arms alongside body, palms flat.

action:

There are 4 complete movements.
Feet together, slowly raise legs to 6 inch above ground. This is *start* position.
1. raise feet to 12 inch above ground. 2. Open legs wide. 3. Close.
4. Lower to position 6 inch above ground. Hold. Repeat from 1.
Notice that after exercise has commenced feet never touch ground.

repetition:

First week: 5. Second week 10. Continue 10, 15 or 20 each session.
Remember feet never touch ground.

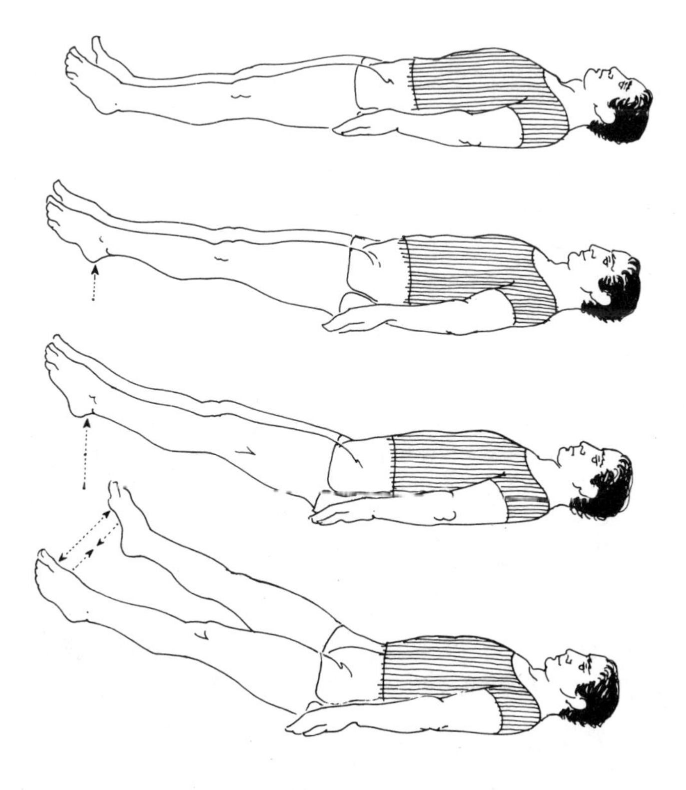

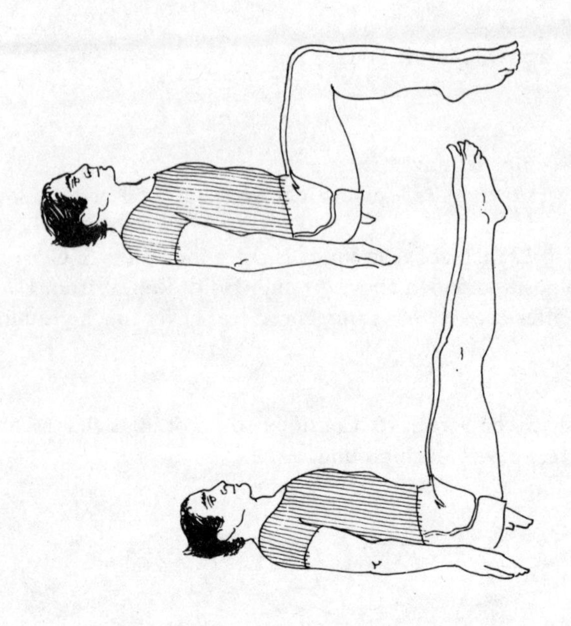

b: stomach firmer

position:

Lie flat on back, arms at sides, palms down.

action:

Raise both knees to vertical line and raise legs to starting position (1). Lower halves will be parallel to ground. Point toes. Now, extend the legs straight up with toes pointing to ceiling and push hard to ensure legs are precisely vertical (2). Lower legs back to 1. Repeat. Feet do not touch ground until completion of routine.

repetition:

Start at 10. Increase to 20. Once you have mastered the correct position the speed of the routine should be taken at 10 per 30 seconds.

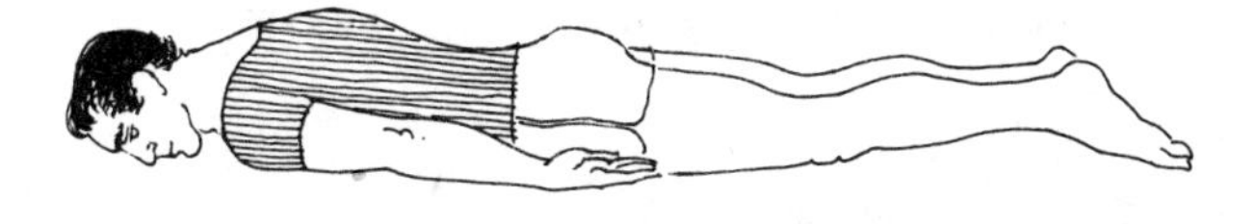

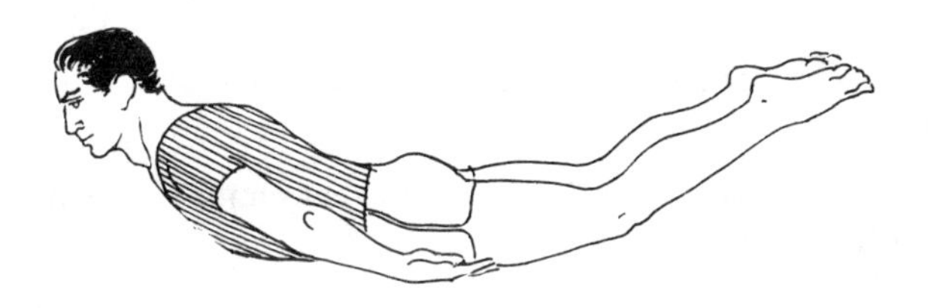

c: back and buttock firmer

position:

Lie face down, palms tucked in under thighs.

action:

Keep legs straight by pointing toes. Raise head, shoulders and both legs at the same time so that body forms a curve. Hold position for a count of 3. Lower to flat. With practice both thighs will lift clear of palms.

repetition:

10 times until it is mastered. Increase to 20.

d: press-ups

This is a well-known exercise for developing strength and muscles, but many men are defeated by it as they set out initially, unfit, collapsing under unaccustomed strain. Therefore there are two routines to choose from: *regular* and *modified.* If you have trouble with the first, try the second. Switch back to the *regular* routine only when you are ready.

position:

Lie flat on stomach with palms placed level with and touching shoulders.

action:

Keeping back straight, concentrate, then straighten arms so that they lift the body clear of the ground.

Regular: in this routine your body must be kept ramrod straight with your arms lifting the body balanced on the toes.

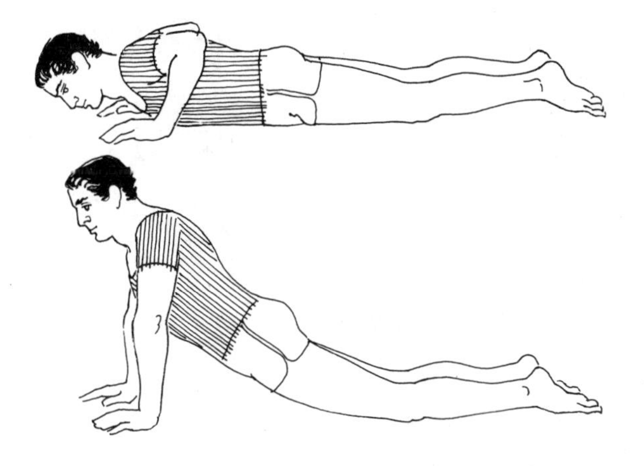

Modified: as before but keep the knees on the ground so the lift is pivoted on the knees.

On reaching the lift position in either routine, count to 3, then lower to the ground ready to lift again.

repetition:

10, graduating to 20.

e. jump from crouch

This is a routine designed to make the efficiency of heart and lungs improve by short bursts of extra exertion while at the same time strengthening the legs. If you are overweight do not include this routine in your workout.

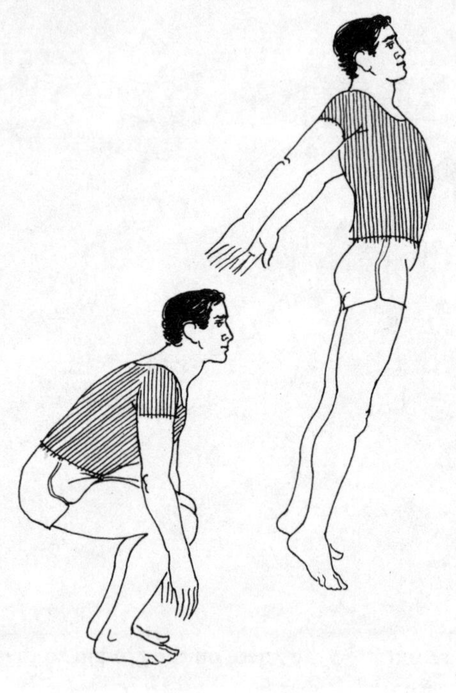

position:

Feet together, heels on the ground. Bend until fingers almost touch the ground.

action:

Jump up in the air, swinging arms backwards. (At the outset do not attempt to jump too high or leap in a manner that strains. Start with small jumps and increase height and vigour as you become fitter over the weeks).

repetition:

10 only. When jumps become easier increase jumps to 15, 20.

3. Keep In Trim

The following are two simple extra exercises that can be carried out as part of the Fitness Plan but are also simple enough to be performed more often. Many men find they are useful routines for relieving tension at the office.

a: knee lift (for stomach)

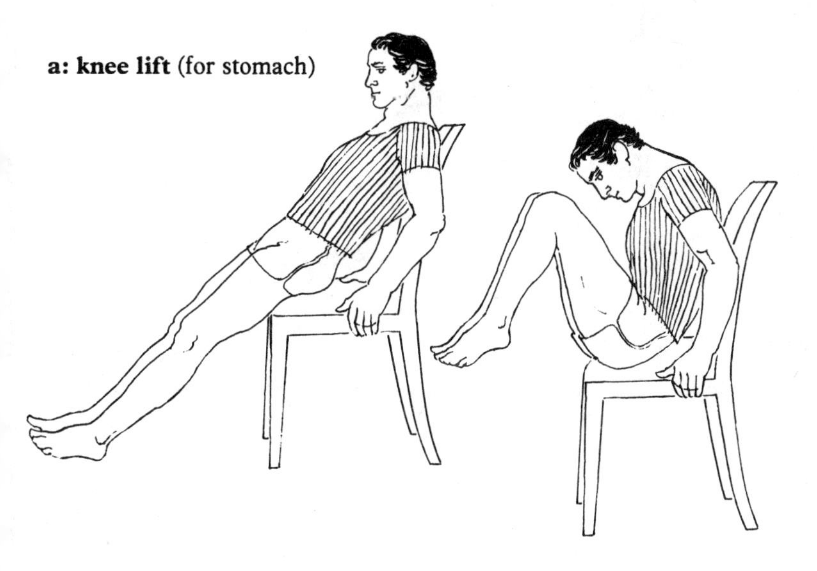

position:

Sit well forward on the chair. Lean back and grip sides of chair.

action:

Gripping tightly, raise knees up towards chest while lowering head to meet knees. Allow back to bend naturally. Exhale as you raise knees, inhale as you lower.

repetition:

Start with 10 or less. Later increase to 15, 20.

b: desk-top press-ups (for arms and chest)

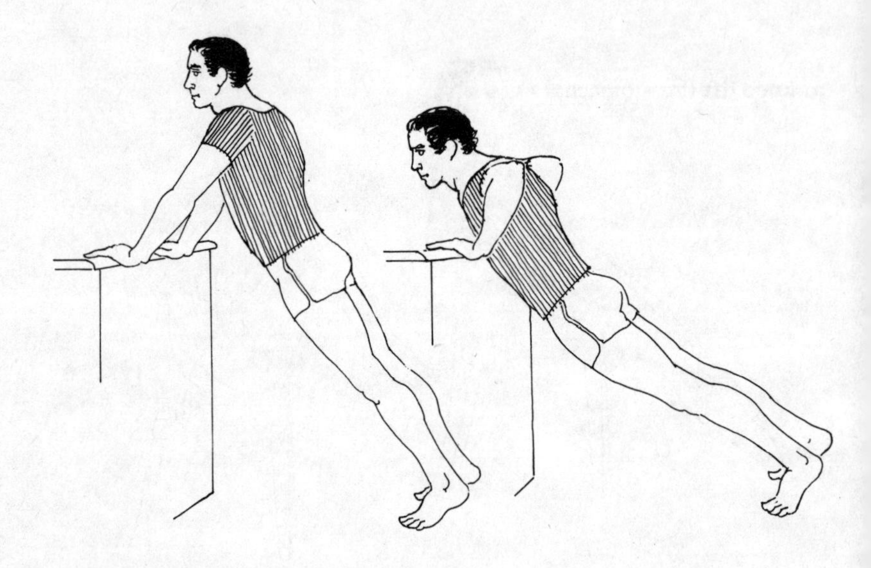

position:

Stand back from desk, feet shoulder width apart. Place hands on desk directly in front, also shoulder width apart.

action:

Bending the arms, slowly lower the body so that chest touches the desk, then, slowly, straighten arms again. Pivot on the toes.

repetition:

10 times. Increase repetitions as routines become easier.

Postscript

And so to the future.

The aim of this book is to help a man get the most from life especially in the period of mid-life transition when the male-menopause threatens to upturn daily life and cause irrational emotional crises. The solution lies in being able to come to terms with yourself and finding ways to be successful while still taking great pleasure in what you are doing.

For many men there are hellish patches of M-M to get through but if as part of survival you base all your plans for the future on the ability to find personal satisfaction at work and at home, you lay down foundations for making the most of middle age. Middle age beckons and the years of getting old are not so far away. It is a sobering thought but there is one further attitude or recommendation worth bearing in mind. It was expressed by Bernard Baruch who lived until ninety-five.

> *'I will never be an old man. To me old age is always fifteen years older than I am.'*

Bibliography

Bednarik, K. *The Male in Crisis* (Alfred A. Knopf)
Bowskill, Derek & Anthea Linacre. *The 'Male' Menopause* (Frederick Muller)
Bromley, D. B. *The Psychology of Human Aging* (Pelican)
Carruthers, Malcolm & Alistair Murray. *F/40 – Fitness on 40 Minutes a Week* (Futura)
Coleman, Dr. Vernon. *Everything you want to know about Aging* (Gordon & Cremonesi)
Comfort, Dr. Alex. *The Joy of Sex* (Mitchell Beazley)
Eating for a healthy heart (Good Housekeeping)
Gagnon, John. *Human Sexualities* (Scott, Foreman)
Kinsey, A. *Sexual Behaviour in the Human Male* (W. B. Saunders)
Llewellyn-Jones, Derek. *Everyman* (OUP)
Llewellyn-Jones, Derek. *Sex and VD* (Faber)
Mayer, Nancy. *The Male-Mid-Life Crisis* (Doubleday)
Masters & Johnson. *Human Sexual Inadequacy* (Bantam Books)
Molloy, John T. *Dress for Success* (Warner)
Morehouse, L. F. & Leonard Gross. *Total Fitness in 30 Minutes a Week* (Futura)
Morton, R. S. *Venereal Disease* (Pelican)
Soddy, Dr. Kenneth. *Men in Middle Life* (Tavistock Publications)
Stay Fit, a 12 Week Men's Fitness Programme (Alfred Publishing)